Handbooks of UK Wastewater Practice

SEWAGE SLUDGE:

INTRODUCING TREATMENT AND MANAGEMENT

Handbooks of UK
Wastewater Practice

SEWAGE SLUDGE:

INTRODUCING TREATMENT AND MANAGEMENT

The Chartered Institution of Water
and Environmental Management

95810
628.16 CHA

© The Chartered Institution of
Water and Environmental Management 1995
ISBN 1 870752 23 6

The Chartered Institution of
Water and Environmental Management
15 John Street, London WC1N 2EB

CONTENTS

FIGURES

PLATES

TABLES

ACKNOWLEDGEMENTS

The Institution gratefully acknowledges the help of the following persons and companies who have made major contributions to the text, and have provided drawings and photographs. Without this willing help the handbook could not have been published.

Chris Avery, Alfa Laval Sharples
BordnaMona Environmental Products UK Ltd. (Plate 6)
Alan Bruce, Consultant
Steve Clay, Severn Trent Water Ltd.
Roger Fuggle, Consultant
David Gibson, Balfour Maunsell Ltd.
Garry Hoyland, Mott MacDonald Water and Environment (Plate 1)
Paul Lowe, Aqua-Enviro
Peter Marsh, Armfibre Ltd. (Plates 4 & 5)
Peter McLoughlin, Simon-Hartley Ltd. (Plate 2)
Peter Matthews, Anglian Water Ltd.
Paperflow Services Ltd. (Fig. 20)
Alan Record, Alfa Laval Sharples Ltd.
Peter Tipping, W. S. Atkins Consultants Ltd.
Stephen Toogood, Specialist in Odour Control
M. J. Warner, Water Engineering Ltd.
Yorkshire Water Services Ltd. (Plate 3)

Author's Note

This publication does not set out to provide an exhaustive survey of systems, but rather to present the broad range of available techniques, together with examples, where appropriate, of available equipment. A mention in the script, or indeed the absence of any mention of any particular equipment, should not be taken by the reader as an endorsement of approval or otherwise of any system.

FOREWORD

The Chartered Institution of Water and Environmental Management (CIWEM) is a corporate learned society and examining body representing the interests of engineers and scientists and other professionally qualified personnel working in the various sectors of the environment: water, air and land. It was formed in July 1987 by the unification of three eminent organizations, The Institution of Public Health Engineers, The Institution of Water Engineers and Scientists, and the Institute of Water Pollution Control, which have a joint history dating back to 1895.

Over the years, the predecessor bodies have produced definitive manuals and other publications, notably in respect of UK practice in the water industry. These have become reference sources for those who are actively engaged in the field, as well as for students seeking authoritative guidance in preparing for professional qualifications. Such publications are being continued by CIWEM, and the range is being extended to take account of the wider environmental interests which the new organization embraces.

During the period 1973–1987, the former Institute of Water Pollution Control published nine handbooks on 'Unit Processes'. Since then, and particularly in the last few years, major new legislation relating to the subject has been introduced in the UK and there have also been some important new developments in operational and management aspects. Accordingly, the handbooks are being completely rewritten to incorporate the changes which have occurred. The overall subject of sewage sludge is now covered in four of these new handbooks, *Introducing Treatment and Management* being the first in the series; the other three companion handbooks, namely *Stabilization and Disinfection; Dewatering, Drying and Incineration,* and *Utilization and Disposal,* deal with the various processes and disposal routes.

The Institution wishes to record its grateful thanks to Nick Sambidge who undertook the task of writing this handbook, to the Editor, Malcom Haigh, and also to the people and companies mentioned in the acknowledgements who have made significant contributions during its preparation.

C. J. A. Binnie
President

August 1995

1. Introduction

Each day in the UK, about 75 000 wet tonnes (3000 dry tonnes) of sewage sludge are produced by the 7400 or so sewage-treatment works serving our cities, towns and smaller communities. While the treated effluents from these works flow into receiving watercourses, the sludge which is produced during treatment (and which may contain well over 50% of the original pollution load in the sewage) has to be retained on the works, forming a completely separate process stream for treatment before being transported to a suitable final site for utilization or disposal.

The volume of liquid sludge produced at a sewage-treatment works usually represents only 1–2% of the total flow of sewage, but its treatment and disposal accounts for 30–50% of the total running costs of the works. The stages of treatment can include screening, disintegration, thickening, stabilization, dewatering and incineration, and usually the selected process will depend upon the method of final disposal.

The need to manage the disposal of sewage sludge as a day-to-day operation has existed in the UK since the mid-nineteenth century when sewage was first treated by processes involving liquid-solid separation. There is, therefore, a long tradition of sludge disposal management in the UK and a great deal of operational experience and knowledge about the subject. However, the challenge in the 1990s is far greater than in earlier years, and it is certain to become even more demanding as the twenty-first century approaches.

Definitions. Sludge has been described[1] as 'a mixture of solids and water produced during the treatment of wastewater'. In UK legislation[2] a more restricted definition is used, and sludge is described as 'residual sludge from sewage plants treating domestic or urban wastewaters and from other sewage plants treating wastewaters of a composition similar to domestic and urban wastewaters'.

The term 'biosolids' is being increasingly used to describe treated sewage sludge suitable for beneficial re-use, and in the USA it is becoming rare to see any mention of 'sludge' in the literature relating to beneficial recycling of such material. At least two UK water companies are using 'biosolids' to describe sludge which is recycled to agriculture, and it seems likely that the word will gain wider general use. Until that time, however, 'sludge' will remain the preferred technical term for the subject of this handbook.

The term 'pretreatment' has been used in this handbook to describe a process which prepares the raw sludge for subsequent treatment, and includes screening or disintegration of the sludge, thickening, and conditioning prior to dewatering.

2. Sludge Production

2.1 Types of Sludge

Sludges from conventional sewage-treatment plants are derived from primary, secondary and tertiary treatment processes and are known as (a) primary sludge, including storm-tank sludge, (b) secondary sludge, and (c) tertiary sludge, respectively (Fig. 1). Where primary and secondary sludges are settled together in primary sedimentation tanks, the mixture is referred to as 'co-settled' sludge.

2.1.1 Primary sludge. Primary sludge, consisting largely of faecal solids, is normally the major proportion of the sludge in terms of dry solids, although the actual proportion varies according to the composition of the sewage, efficiency of primary sedimentation, and whether any settlement aids have been employed, e.g. the addition of flocculating agents. It contains faecal material, paper, items derived from sanitary and medical products, kitchen wastes, grit and other mineral matter. The presence of industrial effluent may have a marked influence on the characteristics of the sludge, depending on the types of industry in the catchment area. It is also likely to contain a variety of pathogenic micro-organisms; therefore there are regulations concerning the manner in which this type of sludge may be used in agriculture.

A typical domestic primary sludge is normally greyish black, has an offensive odour and contains about 5% dry solids (range 3–7%) of which 70–80% is organic and volatile matter.

2.1.2 Humus sludge. Humus sludge is the product of the settlement of effluent from biological filters, and is mainly bacterial and fungal material sloughed from the filter media, together with the living and dead remains of macro-invertebrates such as fly larvae and worms.

Fresh humus sludge is dark brown in colour and has a characteristic earthy smell. A typical sludge contains 0.5–2.0% dry solids (DS) of which 65–75% is organic matter. The rate of production of humus sludge varies seasonally because of the temperature dependency of the grazing fauna in the filters. It is not easily thickened alone, and at most sewage-treatment works the practice is to return humus sludge to the primary sedimentation tanks for co-settlement with the primary sludge.

a) Works giving activated-sludge treatment with separate initial treatment of primary, surplus-activated and tertiary sludges

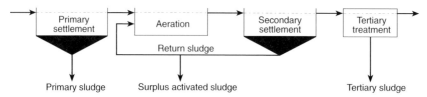

b) Works giving activated-sludge treatment with co-settlement of primary and surplus-activated sludges

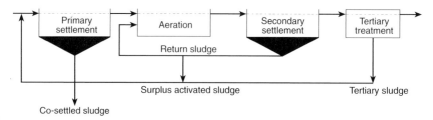

c) Works giving treatment by biological filtration with co-settlement of primary and humus sludge

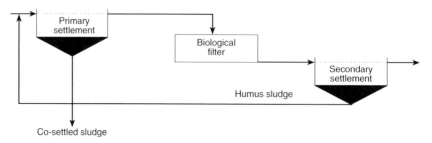

d) Works giving extended aeration treatment of unsettled sewage

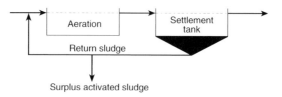

Fig. 1. Sources of sewage sludge

Biological aerated filters and their variations produce a humus sludge which reflects the different types of media and hence biological life, and is closer in character to surplus activated sludge.

2.1.3 Surplus activated sludge. In an activated-sludge plant, polluting matter is transferred to the mixed-liquor suspended solids (MLSS), thereby increasing its mass. A proportion of this is removed at regular intervals in order to maintain the optimum level of MLSS, and is known as surplus activated sludge. It consists of flocculated and synthesized solids and micro-organisms, varies in colour from grey to dark brown, and normally has an earthy smell. Depending upon the rate of recycling and other factors, surplus activated sludge normally contains less than 1% DS of which 70–85% is organic matter; if allowed to stand without aeration it normally becomes black and offensive. Surplus activated sludge, particularly at medium and larger sized works, is thickened separately before passing forward for further treatment.

2.1.4 Tertiary sludge. Tertiary sludge is derived from a tertiary treatment process. It comprises that fraction of the secondary sludge which remains in the effluent from the secondary settlement tank and removed in the tertiary treatment stage. It forms only a very small part of the total sludge production, and is usually returned to the primary sedimentation tanks for co-settlement. Sludge produced during physico-chemical treatment for the removal of nutrients from secondary effluent is included in this category.

2.1.5 Digested sludge. There are two types of digested sludge, which are products of anaerobic and aerobic digestion respectively, although the latter process is not widely used. Anaerobically digested sludge is black, generally inoffensive and has a characteristic tarry odour. Aerobically digested sludge is usually dark brown in colour with an inoffensive, mildly earthy odour. A comparison of the analysis of raw sludge with anaerobically digested sludge is given in Table 1.

Digested sludge may also be produced by 'cold' or psycrophilic anaerobic digestion at ambient temperature, but this process is now of minor importance in the UK. Provided that the sludge has a retention period of three months in a cold digester, it may be considered to be 'effectively treated'.

2.2 Constituents of Sewage Sludge

Sludges from different sewage-treatment works differ widely in character and composition according to the origin of the sewage and the type of treatment processes employed. Examples of some chemical constituents are given in Table 2.

Table 1. Comparison of Analysis of Primary and Digested Sludges

Parameter	Primary sludge	Digested sludge
pH	6.3	7.2
Alkalinity (mg/l)	1200	4400
Volatile acids (mg/l)	2900	<200
Dry solids (%)	5.0	3.0
Petroleum extractable (%)	20	10
Organic and volatile matter (%)	70	60
Nitrogen (as N) (%)	4.3	3.2

A most important general objective is to minimize, as far as is practicable, the concentration of any potentially toxic elements (e.g. heavy metals) in the sludge. This is achieved in most cases by strict control of industrial discharges to the sewerage system. However, it is important to note that some of the metals present in sludge, particularly zinc and copper, are derived from domestic sources.

Total dry solids. Liquid sludge may contain less than 1% or, after thickening, as much as 9% DS; but the usual range for a primary and secondary co-settled sludge is 4–6% DS. After mechanical dewatering the cake will usually contain 25–35% DS.

Table 3 indicates the approximate maximum dry-solids content of different sludges at which they will remain in a liquid state, i.e. will flow reasonably easily from a vessel and through pipes. As the solids content increases above these values, sludges become first of 'paste-like' consistency, and flow only with difficulty. Some sludges, particularly activated sludges, may also demonstrate thixotropic characteristics at certain dry-solids contents.

Organic and volatile solids. The solid matter in the sludge contains 65–80% organic matter (as determined by loss in weight on ignition at 500°C). Included in the loss could be volatile inorganic matter. The calorific value of the organic matter

Table 2. Typical Concentrations (% on DS) of Some Chemical Constituents of Liquid Sludges[3]

Constituent	Primary sludge	Activated sludge	Co-settled sludge
Total nitrogen	3.0	4.0	3.5
Crude protein	23.0	47.0	32.0
Amino-acids plus ammonia	16.5	37.6	24.0
Total phosphorus	2.5	3.5	2.8
Potassium	0.3	0.1	0.2
Fat (ether extractable)	21.0	4.2	14.7
Mineral oil	5.0	nil	0.4
Fibre	19.0	0.4	120.0
Sugars	0.7	nil	0.4
Starches	1.5	nil	0.9
Ash	30.0	20.0	25.0

Vitamins (mg/kg DS)

Thiamine	7.0	7.0	7.0
Riboflavin	1.5	2.0	1.7
B12	1.5	4.0	2.5

in sludge may be exploited by incineration with use of surplus heat to generate power, and by anaerobic digestion and utilization of the digester gas to produce heat and power.

Water content. The water content of liquid sludge is normally in excess of 92% of its mass. It is a burden in terms of volume for handling, storage and disposal, although retaining a sludge in liquid form is clearly an advantage in terms of distribution over land and dispersal at sea.

Nutrients. In addition to the beneficial effects on soil structure and water-

Table 3. Approximate Maximum Dry-Solids Content of Sludges

Sludge	Maximum solids in liquid state (% DS)	Normal working range (% DS)
Raw primary	10	3–7
Raw co-settled	12	3–7
Digested co-settled	12	3–6
Raw activated	4–5	1–3

retention properties, the principle benefit of sludge when applied to farmland is the presence of nitrogen, phosphorus and a small amount of potash. The amounts vary between different sludges, but in a domestic sludge the concentrations may be 3%, 2%, and 0.3% respectively. In practice, the nitrogen and phosphorus content of a sludge usually represents its greatest 'value' in terms of the savings which can be made in agriculture by using it to replace artificial fertilizers.

Heavy metals. The concentration of certain heavy metals (zinc, copper, nickel, cadmium, lead, mercury, chromium) and other potentially toxic elements (molybdenum, selenium, arsenic, fluoride) are of major significance when the sludge is to be disposed of to agriculture, and to a lesser extent to other methods of disposal. Typical figures are given in Table 4.

Table 4. Typical Composition of Domestic Sewage Sludge (concentrations in mg/kg)

Zn	Cu	Ni	Cr	Cd	Pb	Hg
800	330	30	40	5	230	2

Pathogens. Untreated sludge will always contain pathogenic and parasitic micro-organisms, although the numbers will depend on the state of health of the population. Basic hygiene precautions are essential to those involved in sewage and sludge treatment operations.

Persistent organic compounds. These are non-degradable (and therefore persistent) synthetic organic compounds derived from industrial effluents. Some could be hazardous to humans, animals or plants, but concentrations are so low that there is a negligible risk to health. However, there is an increasing awareness of these substances, particularly when the sludge is to be used in agriculture.

Plant seeds. The seeds of some cultivated plants (particularly tomatoes) are likely to be present in most sludges, and they may cause problems if their germination and growth is undesirable. Weed seeds are also a potential problem when sludge is used as a fertilizer.

2.3 Sludge Quantities

At most sewage-treatment works about 60–70% of the suspended solids (SS) and 20–30% of the biochemical oxygen demand (BOD) in the sewage arriving at the works are removed by primary sedimentation. Up to 80% of the BOD remaining in the sewage after primary sedimentation is converted into an equivalent weight of solids during biological treatment and removed by settlement. The total quantity of sludge formed includes primary and secondary (biological) sludge, and when a tertiary-treatment or nutrient-removal process is employed, a further quantity of sludge is produced.

Sludge production data cannot be expected to be highly accurate, and the difficulty of measuring sludge quantities precisely, particularly at smaller works, is well known. More recently there has been an improvement in the veracity of data as a result of the legal necessity to maintain registers showing the origin and destination of stated quantities of sludge used in agriculture and related outlets.

In the latter half of the 1990s and the early years of the twenty-first century, a substantial increase in UK sludge production is inevitable as a result of the implementation of the EC urban wastewater Directive[4]. There may also be a trend towards increased *per capita* sludge production in future years as living standards rise, although the likely significance of this is difficult to predict. Fig. 2 shows how, in 1991, sludge was disposed of between the major outlets, and makes the comparison with the predicted situation for 1999.

Predictions for 1999 are difficult to make, and it can be seen from Fig. 2 that the

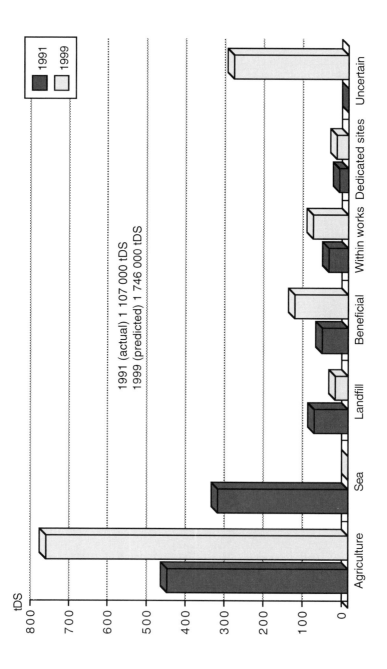

Fig. 2. Sludge production, 1991 and 1999

category of 'uncertain' is a significant amount. The predicted total sludge production of 1.746 million tDS for 1999 represents an increase over 1991 of 58%.

Using the *per capita* sludge production values listed in Table 5, and the size of the populations served by sewage-treatment works providing differing degrees of treatment, calculations can be made of the annual sludge production throughout the UK or in individual regions. The basis of the calculation is shown in Appendix 1.

2.3.1 Primary sludge. The amount of dry solids in primary sludge will depend upon the concentration of SS in the sewage, the settleability of those solids, the efficiency of the sedimentation tank, and whether internal liquors are returned to the inlet. Primary sludge production can be calculated from:

(i)   Measurement of the quantity of SS in the primary sedimentation tank inflow and outflow;

(ii) The SS loading multiplied by the proportion settling in the primary sedimentation tanks; or

(iii) An assumed *per capita* SS figure and an assumed percentage reduction in the primary sedimentation tanks. (In the absence of specific data a design figure of 65% reduction may be used.)

The average concentration of SS can be assessed by taking continuous or frequent periodic (e.g. hourly) samples over a number of 24-hour periods, taking account of seasonal variations due to holidays and weekends, and variations due to intermittent industrial operations.

Where analytical data are not available, a *per capita* estimate of domestic sludge production may be made from experience in the area, or, a generally acceptable figure for the amount of dry suspended matter in domestic sewage is 0.06–0.07 kg/head. d. The industrial proportion should be calculated by sampling the industrial effluents. Any proposed industrial development must also be taken into account.

2.3.2 Humus sludge. A difficulty in estimating the sludge yield from biological filters arises from the marked seasonal variation in biological activity and hence sludge production. For example, it has been shown[5] that for a low-rate filter treating domestic sewage, the rate of humus sludge production in the spring was six times greater than in the summer months.

The yield also depends upon the type of plant; for example, low-rate filters produce less humus sludge than high-rate filters. The average sludge yield from low-rate biological filters is normally 0.25–0.50 kg DS/kg BOD removed, less the

**Table 5. Typical Sludge Production Rates
(normal range in parenthesis)**

Sludge	Total dry solids (g/head. d)	Organic and volatile (% dry solids)
Primary	52 (50–54)	70 (62–75)
Surplus activated	30 (25–35)	80 (75–85)
Humus	22 (15–30)	75 (70–80)
Co-settled (primary + activated)	82 (75–90)	75
Co-settled (primary + humus)	74 (65–84)	72
Digested * (primary + activated)	51	60
Digested * (primary + humus)	47	56

* Assuming anaerobic digestion destroys 50% of volatile matter

dry mass of SS in the humus tank effluent; whereas the average yield from high-rate filters may be as high as 10 kg DS/kg BOD removed. The seasonal rate of humus sludge production varied in the case of one low-rate filter from 0.5 kg/kg BOD removed during the spring to as low as 0.08 kg/kg BOD removed during the summer. The overall yearly average rate was 0.22 kg/kg BOD removed.

2.3.3 Surplus activated sludge. *Conventional activated sludge (5–16 h aeration).* The surplus sludge dry solids yield is often taken as 0.6–0.8 kg DS/ kg BOD applied in the settled sewage, less the dry mass of SS in the secondary settlement tank effluent. In the absence of other data, a reduction of 30% in BOD as a result of primary sedimentation may be assumed.

High-rate activated sludge (less than 5 h aeration). For a typical high-rate activated-sludge process, the total surplus sludge dry solids yield may be as high as 0.8–1.0 kg DS/kg BOD applied in the settled sewage, less the dry mass of SS in the secondary settlement tank effluent.

Extended-aeration activated sludge (>20 h aeration). Primary sedimentation is not normally used upstream of extended aeration. Sludge production from this process may be assumed to be 0.4–0.6 kg DS/kg BOD applied in the crude sewage, less the dry mass of SS in the secondary tank effluent.

2.3.4 Tertiary sludge. Where tertiary treatment is used, the dry mass of solids captured by this process and returned for treatment and disposal should be added to the quantity of humus or surplus activated sludge.

2.3.5 Digested sludge. When primary or mixed sludge undergoes anaerobic digestion, the organic and volatile matter is normally reduced by about 50% with a consequent overall reduction in the mass of total solids of 35–40%. To reduce the actual volume for further treatment, supernatant liquor is removed.

Typical *per capita* daily rates of production of the main types of sludge, together with the typical proportions of organic and volatile matter, produced by sewage-treatment works in the UK, are given in Table 5.

2.3.6 European sludge production. The domestic population of the European Community is 345 million. The four countries France, Germany, Italy and the UK produce 84% of the sludge produced in the EC. Table 6 shows the most recent estimate of sludge production in the member states[6].

2.4 Product Options

Modern processing technology can be used to convert raw sludge into many types of end-product to meet particular disposal or utilization requirements. Fig. 3 shows the twelve main types which can be produced in practice and the train of treatment operations and processes required to produce them. The degree of processing required to form the final sludge product may range from 'none' (or screening and/ or consolidation only) in which case the product for disposal is 'liquid untreated sludge', to several stages of treatment resulting in a product which is markedly different from the original raw liquid sludge (e.g. compost or incinerator ash).

Although at least twelve types of sludge can be produced, Table 7 shows that, in practice in the early 1990s, over 90% of UK production was represented by types 1 to 6 inclusive and, of these, 'liquid digested sludge' was the major single product type. It should be noted that the distinction made in the list between 'untreated' and 'stored' sludges is important mainly in relation to their subsequent use in agriculture, and not necessarily with regard to other means of disposal.

If incinerator ash is included, over 98% of the UK's total sludge production is represented. However, while the remaining five products (types 7–11) currently

Table 6. EC Population and Sludge Disposal, 1991–92

Country	Population (million)	Connected to sewer (%)	Connected to STW (%)	Sludge disposed (tDS/a $\times 10^3$)	Sludge disposed (g/head.d)
Belgium	9.9	70	28	59	58
Denmark	5.1	93	92	170	99
France	56.9	65	50	852	82
Germany	79.7	89	83	2681	111
Greece	10.2	45	34	48	40
Ireland	3.5	67	45	37	64
Italy	57.7	75	60	816	65
Luxembourg	0.4	97	87	8	62
Netherlands	15.0	97	88	323	67
Portugal	9.9	52	20	25	35
Spain	39.0	70	59	350	42
UK	57.5	96	85	1107	62
Total	344.8			6476	

represent very small outputs in national terms, they are often important on a local scale (e.g. thermally dried sludge or compost). Some of these products might feature more prominently in future UK practice as environmental and other pressures increase. It is certain that some significant changes in sludge-treatment practices on a national scale will occur in the mid to late 1990s as a result of the banning of sludge disposal to sea by 1999. It has been predicted[4] that 22% of UK sludge will be incinerated by 1999, and this will reduce the proportion of sludge disposed of in the 'liquid untreated' form. There is also likely to be a significant increase in the proportion of UK sludge which is processed to the 'liquid digested' or 'dewatered digested' forms as utilization in agriculture and related outlets increase.

As indicated in Table 7, each type of sludge product has particular characteristics

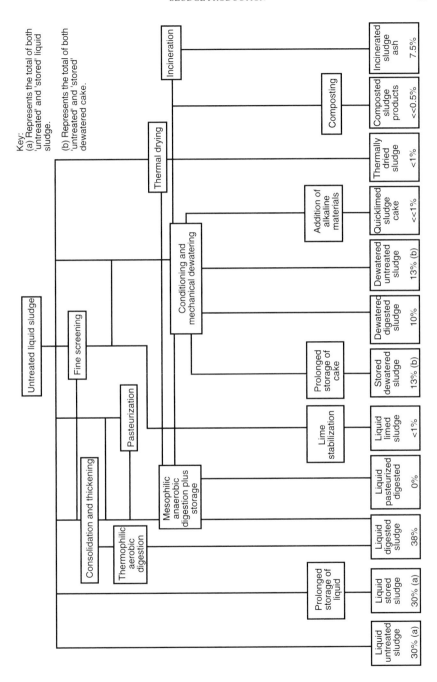

Key:
(a) Represents the total of both 'untreated' and 'stored' liquid sludge.

(b) Represents the total of both 'untreated' and 'stored' dewatered cake.

Fig. 3. Treatment processes for producing twelve types of sludge

Table 7. Main Types of Sludge Product and Outlets

Type	Sludge product	Proportion of UK production (%)	Options for utilization or disposal
1 2	Liquid untreated Liquid stored	30*	A, F, R, L, S
3 4	Dewatered untreated Stored dewatered	13*	A, F, R, L
5	Liquid digested	38	A, F, R, L, S
6	Dewatered digested	10	A, F, R, L
7	Pasteurized digested	<<0.5	A
8	Lime stabilized	<1	A
9	Alkaline dry product	<<1	A, R, L
10	Compost product	<<0.5	A, R, L, M
11	Thermally dried	<1	A, R, L, M
12	Incinerator ash	7.5	L, SP

* Relative proportions of types 1, 2, 3, and 4 are not available.

Key
(A) Use in agriculture   (F) Use in forestry and woodlands   (R) Use in reclamation
(L) Disposal to landfill   (S) Disposal to sea   (M) Public amenity areas
(SP) Special products, e.g. building products, soils, etc.

which render it more, or less, suitable for a given means of utilization or disposal, and these are described in detail in the companion handbooks *Sewage Sludge: Stabilization and Disinfection; Dewatering, Drying and Incineration;* and *Utilization and Disposal.*

2.5 Major Outlets

The three major outlets for sludge in the UK in the early to mid-1990s were (a) agriculture, (b) sea disposal, and (c) landfill, which together accounted for almost 90% of total national production. Table 8 shows the quantities of sludge disposed of by means of various outlets[7].

2.5.1 Agriculture. Table 8 demonstrates the importance of the agricultural outlet

Table 8. Quantities of Sludge to Various Outlets during 1993–94 (Descending in order of quantity)

Region	Agriculture		Landfill		Incineration (a)		Sea		Other (b)		Total	
	000s tDS	%	000s tDS	%	000s tDS	%	000s tDS	%	000s tDS	%	000s tDS	%
Thames	104	55	0	0	0	0	74	39	11	6	189	19
Severn Trent	85	51.5	43	26	28	17	0	0	9	5.5	165	16
Anglian	108	78	4	3	0	0	12	9	15	11	139	14
North West	31	24.5	18	14	9	7	66	52	2	1.5	126	12
Yorkshire	47	41	18	16	41	36	8	7	0	0	114	11
Scotland	13	16	5	6	1	1	60	75	1	1	80	8
Southern	33	58	2	3	5	9	8	14	9	16	57	5.5
Wessex	27	87	0	0	0	0	0	0	4	13	31	3
Dwr Cymru	23	79	0	0	0	0	5	17	1	3.5	29	3
Northumbrian	3	8	12	32	0	0	20	54	2	6	37	3.5
N. Ireland	16	50	2	6	0	0	14	44	0	0	32	3
South West	12	80	0	0	0	0	3	20	0	0	15	1.5
UK Total	502	50	104	10	84	8	270	27	54	5	1014	100

(a) Disposed of as ash. Quantity expressed as tDS of sludge before incineration. Actual quantity of ash would be 25–35% of the sludge tDS. (b) Includes forestry, land reclamation, amenity use, within curtilage of sewage works, etc.

accounting for 50% of the national production and representing a population of over

27 million people. However, while the overall importance of agriculture is clear, the relative dependence on this outlet varies considerably from region to region. In some regions (e.g. Wessex, South West, Welsh and East Anglian) the agricultural outlet represents over 75% of regional production while in other regions (e.g. Northumbrian and Scotland) it is less than 20%, mainly due to the major use of sea disposal.

Although agricultural use is of major importance, the total area of farmland on which sludge is applied is relatively very small. The national survey[4] showed that the total area of land utilized in 1990-91 was 52 000 ha, which represents only 0.3% of the total area of agricultural land in the UK.

2.5.2 Sea disposal. This outlet has been of major importance for many years and will remain so until close to the date of its cessation at the end of 1998. However, the table shows how the degree of dependence on this route varies considerably from region to region.

By the end of 1998 at the latest, sludge which was disposed of to sea in the mid-1990s will require land-based outlets. Predictions indicate that the agricultural outlet and other beneficial uses will receive about half of this sludge, with the remainder being transported to landfill (as ash) after incineration. As one consequence of the overall increase in national sludge production, the total tonnage of sludge which will be used beneficially in the latter half of the 1990s is predicted to increase substantially.

2.5.3 Landfill. This was the third most important outlet representing about 10% of production. However, this proportion relates only to deposition of 'whole' sludge. If the 8% of sludge which was incinerated and the ash disposed of to landfill, is included, the percentage of sludge to landfill is closer to 20%. As with other outlets, however, the dependence on landfill varies widely between different regions.

3. Consolidation and Thickening

3.1 Introduction

Thickening and dewatering are processes for separating water from sludge; their essential difference is in the amount of water separated. The purpose of thickening is to produce a sludge which can be readily handled, pumped and mixed but has a much lower volume, and therefore the cost of providing and operating downstream treatment and disposal processes (such as digestion and transport) is reduced. Thickening is also used as the first stage in dewatering. With the economic benefits to be derived from thickening, the process is used at most sewage-treatment works.

For a unit weight of solids, sludge containing 5% DS occupies only one-fifth of the volume of a sludge containing 1% DS. Table 9 demonstrates the relationship of the dry-solids content to the volume of sludge, within both the 'thickening' and 'dewatering' ranges, and was derived from the simple equation:

$$\frac{Initial\ volume\ (V1)}{Final\ volume\ (V2)} = \frac{Final\ sludge\ thickness\ (S2)}{Initial\ sludge\ thickness\ (S1)}$$

The importance of thickening sludge is amply demonstrated in Table 9, where $100\ m^3$ are reduced to $20\ m^3$ when thickened from 1% to 5% DS. However, further consolidation to 10% removes only another $10\ m^3$ of water.

Table 9. Reducing Volume with Increasing Thickness

DS	1%	2%	4%	5%	7%	10%	25%	30%	35%
m^3	100	50	25	20	14	10	4	3.3	2.8

Basically there are four common sludge thickening processes: gravity consolidation, centrifugation, filtration and flotation. These processes differ in the mechanism of separation which may be consolidation or filtration, and in the process driving force which may be gravitational, centrifugal, or mechanical. The associations between these processes, mechanisms and driving forces are given in Table 10.

Table 10. Mechanisms and Driving Forces in Thickening Processes

Process	Mechanism	Driving force
Gravity consolidation	Consolidation	Gravity
Centrifugation	Consolidation	Centrifugal force
Filtration	Filtration	Gravity and/or applied pressure
Flotation	Filtration and consolidation	Gravity

The magnitude of the driving force for each process determines the maximum degree of thickening which is obtainable. In principle, the centrifugation and filtration processes, in which the driving force is derived mechanically, have the potential to produce much thicker sludges than the gravity consolidation and flotation processes in which the force is limited by gravity. For example, a centrifuge has to operate well below its capability to thicken sludge, whereas a gravity consolidation tank is required to perform near its optimum.

3.2 Consolidation

In normal practice, the term 'consolidation' refers to the process of gravity consolidation; gravity thickening is another term in common use. Consolidation is used at most sewage-treatment works, and in tanks usually fitted with rotating picket fences. With well-designed equipment and amenable sludges, the process is capable of thickening sewage sludges to the typical concentrations given in paragraph 3.2.3.

3.2.1 Mechanism. Solids suspended in sewage sludge carry electrostatic charges which attract water with a mass many times greater than that of the solids, causing the solids and the water to aggregate into comparatively large particles called flocs. The water incorporated into the flocs is referred to as 'bound' water, and the water in the pores between the flocs is called 'free' water. Typically, the weight of the bound water is about 20 times greater than the weight of the solids.

Flocs containing sewage solids and water are denser than water, and can therefore settle under a gravitational force. Settlement brings the flocs closer together so that water is displaced upwards. In dilute sludges, the flocs settle separately and only the free water is displaced. This process is known as 'hindered' settlement and occurs in the clarification zone of thickening tanks. Consolidation starts when the flocs become contiguous so that further thickening requires bound water to be displaced from inside the flocs, as well as free water from between the flocs. The transition from settling to consolidation, characterized by a sharp decline in the thickening rate, is known as the compaction point. The dry-solids concentration at the compaction point is typically 1.5% for activated sludge and 2.5% for primary sludge.

In consolidation, the gravitational force acting on the solids is transmitted downwards from floc to floc, imposing a compacting pressure which increases with depth. This pressure deforms the flocs, expelling water which is displaced upwards. At the interface between the top-water and the sludge, there is no compacting pressure and the sludge is at the compaction point. At the bottom of the tank, the compacting pressure and hence solids concentration are at their maximum values.

3.2.2 Consolidation curve. The course of consolidation is best explained with reference to batch consolidation. Fig. 4 shows a typical batch consolidation curve for a sewage sludge which has been pre-thickened above the compaction point. The curve shows how the height of the sludge blanket, i.e. the distance from the tank bottom to the top-water/sludge interface, changes with time. The dry-solids concentration of the sludge is inversely proportional to the height of the blanket.

Initially, consolidation seems slow to start, although the suspended solids near the bottom of the tank consolidate rapidly during this period. However, the water displaced upwards dilutes the solids near the top of the blanket, giving the overall impression of little activity.

After the dilution at the blanket top is complete, blanket height decreases at a constant rate. During this period, the thickening propagates upwards from the tank floor. As the consolidation nears completion, the rate declines and blanket height approaches an asymptote. However, sewage sludge consolidation rarely progresses this far because the sludge undergoes anaerobic degradation, producing biogas which then forms bubbles inside and on the flocs. The bubbles reduce the apparent weight of the flocs and destroy the driving force for the process. Eventually, the driving force reverses in direction, causing solids to float.

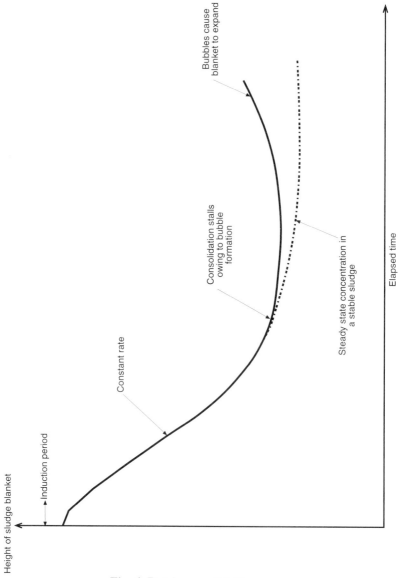

Fig. 4. Batch consolidation curve

3.2.3 Design of consolidation tanks. The main objective of design is to maximize the degree of consolidation without risking a significant loss of performance through biological activity. The retention time of sludge in the consolidation tank has therefore to be limited. When retained for too long, the biological activity will lower the performance of the thickener and also cause the concentration of the degradation products (such as dissolved organic matter, fines, ammonia and sulphides in the top-water) to increase substantially. Since the top-water is usually recycled for treatment, these degradation products, when present in high concentrations, can significantly impair the performance of the main sewage-treatment processes.

Mode of operation. Consolidation can be carried out by batch and continuous modes. In the batch mode, sludge consolidates for a specific time; the top-water is run off either through a floating arm or through openings in the tank wall, and the thick sludge is withdrawn from the bottom of the tank. In the continuous mode, thin sludge is added continuously to the top-water, the thick sludge is continuously removed from the bottom of the tank and the top-water flows continuously over a weir at the top of the tank. However, because of practical limitations, the process is likely to be intermittent.

For most sewage sludges, continuous consolidation has a superior performance compared with batch consolidation and, in general, is the preferred option, although the continuous process has to be soundly designed and operated if the enhanced performance is to be realized.

Tank characteristics. The main design parameters for the continuous mode are the specific plan area and tank depth, and the main parameters for the batch mode are specific plan area and sludge retention time. The specific plan area (SPA) which is measured in $m^2.day/tSS$, is determined by dividing the plan area of a consolidation tank by the loading of suspended solids. The main performance parameters are the dry-solids concentration of the thickened sludge and the strength of the top-water.

A test for evaluating the design and performance parameters has been developed by the Water Research Centre[8] which comprises a series of bench-scale centrifugal batch consolidations, accompanied by a pilot-scale batch consolidation carried out on representative samples of the sludge. Although the test is performed in the batch mode, the results show how the specific plan area and depth of tank, operating in both the continuous and batch modes, affect the dry-solids concentration of the thickened sludge. The test can also indicate the strength of the top-water, although not for continuous operation.

Experience has shown that, for most sewage sludges, tanks can be designed on the basis of generalized SPA values depending on sludge type, and these values are listed in Table 11[9]. If an optimum design is required together with an improved performance prediction, then the tests should be carried out.

Table 11. General Sizing and Performance Criteria for Consolidation Tanks

Type of sludge	SPA (m^2.day/ tSS)	SS of thickened sludge (%)
Primary	9–12	5.5–9.0
Primary + humus	10–15	5.0–8.0
Primary + activated	16–20	3.5–6.5
Humus	35–50	3.0–4.5
Activated	40–60	2.5–3.5

In principle, continuous-flow consolidation tanks can be any depth greater than 3.5–4.0 m, irrespective of the plan area of the tank and the concentration of solids in the feed sludge. Such a depth provides 1 m for the raking zone at the bottom of the tank, 1.0–1.5 m for the consolidating blanket, 1.0–1.5 m for the clarification zone at the top of the tank and at least 0.5 m for operational flexibility.

For a consolidation tank operated in the batch mode, the design depth, H_b (m) is inversely proportional to the dry-solids concentration of the feed sludge, SS_i (kg/m^3) as follows:

$$H_b = 1000 \text{ T}/(SPA - SS_i) \qquad (1)$$

where T is the design retention time (days). Suitable retention times are 1 day for primary and mixed sludges and 2 days for secondary sludges. Consolidating sludges for a longer period may result in the loss of performance, especially during warm weather when biological activity is likely to be high.

Picket fence. Picket fences are virtually indispensable to both batch and continuous consolidation. The general performance criteria only apply when consolidations are assisted by soundly designed picket fences. Table 12 summarizes the process design criteria for picket fences.

As the name implies, a picket fence comprises a series of vertical rods supported on a structure which spans the consolidation tank. When rotated about the centre of the tank, picket fences (a) increase the consolidation rate by creating vertical voids for the passage of the separated water, and (b) release micro-bubbles from the flocs, allowing them to rise to the surface[10].

Although bubbles are released, some remain in the sludge. Picket fences may therefore prolong the effective thickening time but do not necessarily allow consolidations to proceed to completion.

Picket fences in continuous consolidation tanks incorporate a ploughing system which transports the thickened sludge across the floor of the tank to the sludge outlet. The design of this system is crucial to the thickening performance of the tank and is described later.

Torque. In normal operation, the maximum torque required to turn the picket fence occurs at start-up; the running torque is lower because the sludge in the tank rotates with the picket fence, reducing the differential speed. In principle, the torque, T (Nm), on a fence is given by:

$$T = \sum (A\ \sigma\ r) \tag{2}$$

where A is the projected area (m^2) of any particular component of the fence and r (m) is the length of the lever arm to the component. The shear stress, σ (N/m^2), acting on the component, depends on the rheological properties of the sludge at the particular position in the tank. Clearly, the equation is extremely difficult to evaluate. A simple alternative is to relate torque to the diameter, D (m), of the consolidation tank as follows:

$$T = k\ D^2 \tag{3}$$

where k (N/m) is a constant with a value related to the type of sludge. The stress acting on the fence rotating in sewage sludges is not sensitive to the speed of the fence so that speed does not appear in the equation. Maximum torque occurring at start-up may be calculated from the k values given in Table 13. These values are applicable to fences which accord with the design criteria in Table 12, for use in both continuous and batch tanks, and a safety factor of 25–50% should be applied. Picket fences have to be protected against high torques which arise unexpectedly, and a suitable protection system is a torque limiter placed between the motor drive and the gearbox.

Table 12. Design Criteria for Picket Fences

Design aspect	Recommendation	Comments
Peripheral speed	3–6 m/min	Speeds > 10 m/min cause turbulence; speeds < 3 m/min may be effective
No of radial arms	2	Fences with 1 or 3 arms have been used
Picket cross-section	Circular or angle iron	Any cross-section is probably suitable
Picket width	50–60 mm	Suitable range is probably wider
Picket pitch	300–400 mm	No performance data outside this range
Picket height	Pickets should extend from surface to as close to floor as possible	Pickets can clear scum
Picket position	Staggered on opposite arms	Gives improved coverage of sludge
Fixed fence	Do not include	Fixed fence impairs performance
Fence support	Minimize projected area of horizontal fitments	Large area in horizontal plane may reduce effectiveness of vertical pickets
Fence reversal	Stop fence every (say) 6 h, rest for 15 s, reverse for 1 revolution	Reversal keeps fence free of thick sludge and debris

Ploughing systems. A soundly designed ploughing system is crucial to obtaining

Table 13. Values of k Giving Maximum Start-up Torque

Type of sludge	k (N/m)
Primary	110
Primary activated mixture	70–110
Activated	40
Humus	50

good performance from continuous consolidation tanks, in terms of both the thickness of the underflow and quality of the top-water. Its purpose is to plough thickened sludge from the bottom of the blanket to the withdrawal point(s) as directly as possible and with the minimum of disturbance. The following explains the basic principle of the design of ploughing systems for circular consolidation tanks with sludge withdrawal at the centre. However, the principle is the same for tanks with the sludge withdrawal point positioned at the periphery or elsewhere in the tank.

Ploughing systems for consolidation tanks normally comprise vertical steel ploughs or blades attached to the underside of the lower beam of the picket fence, and are inclined at an angle to the radius. The beam supports several blades spaced between the tank centre and the wall, and the bottom edges of the blades have a close tolerance fit to the tank floor.

In principle, the system may have one or two sludge withdrawal points, and these may be located at any position at the tank bottom, either in the floor or wall. The two most common arrangements comprise one withdrawal point, either at the tank centre or the wall. A central withdrawal point requires a substantial well to be provided around the outlet. Peripheral withdrawal prolongs the retention of the sludge in the tank and should not be used in tanks which have a diameter of more than 10 m.

In a sludge blanket consolidating ideally, the vertical downward flow rate of thickened sludge from the bottom of the blanket has the same value irrespective of the position in plan. On reaching the bottom of the tank, thickened sludge has to be turned through a right angle and then travel horizontally to the outlet. In a circular tank with a central outlet, this horizontal flow follows a roughly spiral course to the centre. At any radial position r (m), the total radial component of this flow rate, V_r (m³/s), is given by:

$$V_r = V_o(1 - (r/R)^2) \tag{4}$$

where V_o (m³/s) is the flow rate of thickened sludge at the tank centre and R (m) is the tank radius. The value of V increases parabolically from zero at the wall to V_o at the centre, and has to be evenly matched at every radial position by the capacity of the ploughs. Where the capacity is greater than the required duty, the blades will induce mixing in the blanket, and, where capacity is less, sludge will be drawn down from the blanket. Thus, poor design of the ploughing blades can severely impair thickening performance.

Plough capacity. Fig. 5 shows the basis of a principle derived by Warden[11] for determining the ploughing capacity of blades.

Suppose a blade, inclined at an angle, α, to the radius moves at a tangential velocity of U (m/s). The principle states that the blade induces a flow which is perpendicular to the blade. It follows that the velocity of this induced flow is U cos α. This principle can be applied in several ways depending on the shape and configuration of the blades. The following shows how to apply the principle to chevron-type blades. Assuming that blade height and length are H (m) and L (m) respectively, the flow rate, V (m³/s), of the induced flow is given by:

$$V = L\,H\,E\,U\,\cos \alpha \tag{5}$$

where E is the fractional ploughing efficiency. The linear velocity, U (m/s), of the blade is related to the angular velocity, ω (radians/s) and the radial distance, r (m) by:

$$U = r\,\omega \tag{6}$$

Also, the change in the radial distance, Δr (m), over the blade length, L (m), is given by:

$$\Delta r = L \cos \alpha \tag{7}$$

Furthermore, the blade assembly (picket fence) may comprise N radial arms. Therefore it follows from these equations that the total induced flow rate at any radial distance is given by:

$$V = \Delta r\, H\, N\, E\, r\, \omega \qquad (8)$$

The induced flow, V, has a radial component, V_r, and a tangential component, V_t, which, assuming the ploughing efficiency has the same value in both directions, are given by:

$$V_r = V \sin \alpha \qquad (9)$$
$$V_t = V \cos \alpha \qquad (10)$$

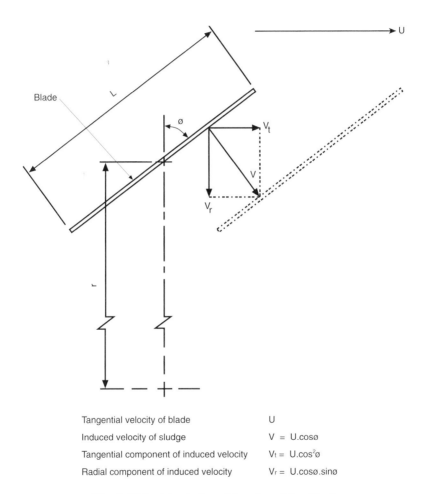

Tangential velocity of blade	U
Induced velocity of sludge	$V = U.\cos\o$
Tangential component of induced velocity	$V_t = U.\cos^2\o$
Radial component of induced velocity	$V_r = U.\cos\o.\sin\o$

Fig. 5. Velocities induced by ploughing blade

Thus, it follows from equations (8) and (9) that the ploughing capacity in the radial direction at any radial position is given by:

$$V_r = \Delta r \, H \, N \, E \, r \, \omega \sin \alpha \tag{11}$$

If the parameters in this equation have constant values, the equation indicates that the radial flow induced by a blade increases with the distance of the blade from the tank centre, contrary to the duty which requires the flow to decrease with radial distance, as indicated by equation (4). This design problem is overcome by inversely relating blade dimensions, i.e. Δr and H, to the radial distance, r.

Combining equations (4) and (11) gives:

$$V_o(1 - (r_1/R)^2) = \Delta r \, H \, N \, E \, r_1 \, \omega \sin \alpha \tag{12}$$

which is a general equation for calculating the dimensions of the ploughing blades depending on the radial distance, r_1 (m), of the blade from the tank centre. The value of r_1 can be taken to be the distance to the trailing (inner) edge of the blade, thereby maximizing the blade size for the particular duty.

The best way to use equation (12) is to calculate the dimensions of consecutive blades, starting with the innermost blade. However, since several ploughing configurations normally have to be investigated before a suitable one is found, the calculations need the assistance of a computer.

Plough blades. For maximum ploughing efficiency, the inclination angle, α, along each blade should be approximately constant at the most effective value. However, geometry prevents straight blades from complying with this requirement, and such blades would be virtually useless if used near the centre of a tank. The shape which complies with the requirement of a constant α is a spiral which is defined by:

$$\tan \alpha \, \ln_e(r/r_1) = \beta - \beta_1 \tag{13}$$

where β (radians) is the angle subtended by the blade at the tank centre and (r_1, β_1) defines the position of the trailing edge of any particular blade. Thus, a spiral is the most effective shape for a blade. The length of a spiral blade along the curve is calculated from the radial span, Δr (m), using equation (7).

The curvature on blades at distances greater than about half a radius from the centre is normally found to be slight, so that these blades can be made straight to simplify construction.

Arrangement of blades. Apart from their dimensions and shape, chevron-type blades may be arranged relative to each other in several ways. An effective arrangement is to place the trailing and leading edges of adjacent blades on the same radius and to make each radial arm of the assembly identical. The bottom edge of the blades should be a close tolerance fit to the tank floor. Typically, the gap should not exceed 10–20 mm at any position on the floor, depending on tank diameter.

Centre well. The centre well is part of the ploughing system, since it allows blades to stop short of the centre and thereby function with an adequate ploughing capacity. In any particular tank, the diameter of the well determines the dimensions of the innermost blade. As a rough guide, the diameter, D_w (m), of the well opening is related to tank diameter, D (m), as follows:

$$D_w = 1 + 0.1D \tag{14}$$

Normally, the sludge withdrawal point is at the bottom of the well on the sidewall. In these cases, the sludge in the centre well should be rotated by the blade assembly so that thickened sludge from all areas of the tank is brought to the withdrawal point. The rotation can be induced by installing vertical pickets on the blade assembly so that they protrude into the well. Well walls are normally inclined at 60°.

Design criteria. Within the design principle, there remains much scope for design variation. Table 14 lists guidance values for the more crucial design parameters. As for picket fences, periodic reversal is needed to prevent sludge and debris binding to the blades.

Table 14. Guidance on Values of Design Parameters for Ploughing Systems

Design aspect	Value
Peripheral speed of arms (Rω)	3–6 m/min
No. of arms (N)	2
Angle of inclination to radius (α)	60°
Floor slope to centre	5–7°
Ploughing efficiency (E)	0.3–0.5
Blade height (H)	150–600 mm
Blade length (L)	750–2000 mm
Blade aspect ratio (L/H)	3–5

Example. Fig. 6 shows an example of a ploughing system designed for a 20 m diameter tank with an average sludge withdrawal rate from the centre well of $15 \, m^3/h$. The peripheral velocity of the system is 5 m/min. Some of the design features described previously are listed as follows:

(i)   The trailing edge of the innermost blade stops at the edge of the well;

(ii)   The inner blades are longer and taller to give an increasing radial flow towards the centre, as required by the duty. The change in height of the inner blades is accommodated by a floor slope of 5° so that the top edges of the blades are approximately at the same elevation, simplifying the construction of the system;

(iii) Blades J to N have the same minimum size, with blade O fitting the end space. To accommodate these blades, the outer annulus of the floor is flat;

(iv)   Trailing and leading edges of consecutive blades are at the same radius; and

(v)   The blades are curved into a spiral shape for maximum ploughing efficiency. However, Blades D to O have only a slight curvature and could be straightened.

Special design features of continuous tanks. In addition to the design features already considered, continuous tanks have other features, and Fig. 7 refers to these. Plate 1 shows a typical installation.

The clarification area is defined as the plan area at the tank top, enclosed between the entry point and the overflow weir. For example, where the feed enters at the tank centre and the tank has a full peripheral weir, the clarification area is equal to the plan area of the tank. Where the feed enters at the tank wall and the weir spans 180°, the clarification area is equal to $(\pi + 2)/2\pi$ times the tank plan area. The shortest distance between the entry point and the weir should not be less than the tank radius.

The feed sludge should enter the tank about 0.5 m below the surface, and must not disturb the sludge blanket sufficiently to impair performance. The upward velocity induced in the clarification zone by the feed flow should be as low as possible and less than 0.5 m/h, although higher velocities may have to be tolerated in tanks receiving dilute activated sludges.

Outward-facing weirs are not effective when the blanket surface is close to the top-water surface and should not be used. The conventional, single-sided, inward-facing weir is preferred.

Scum collecting at the water surface and on the weir plate should be removed to maintain efficiency. The scum may be encouraged to flow over the weir with the

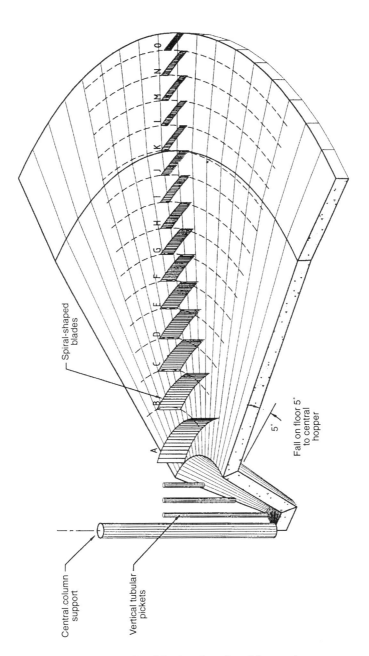

Fig. 6. Example of design for ploughing system

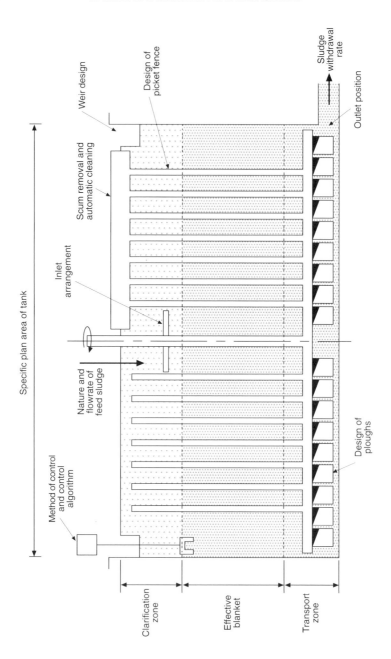

Fig. 7. Design aspects of a continuous consolidation tank

top-water or into a chute for separate collection. Care should be exercised in designing and maintaining these systems, since many fail to work effectively. Radial scum-boards impair clarification and should not be used.

Plate 1. View of ploughing blades in large continuous consolidation tank

3.2.4 Operation of continuous-flow tanks. The feed sludge must be fresh and dilute. Primary feed sludge should have a dry-solids concentration of less than 3% and should be pumped directly from the sedimentation tanks to the consolidation tank. If continuous feeding is impracticable, pumping should be timed to transfer batches at intervals of 4 h or less.

Effective control of the blanket height is crucial. The aim is to keep the top of the blanket at or near a particular elevation, irrespective of the day-to-day variations in the loading and consolidation characteristics of the sludge solids.

In its simplest form, the control system comprises a single ultrasonic solids sensor positioned at the required elevation, typically 2.0–2.5 m from the tank floor. The system works by starting the desludging pump at pre-set intervals and then running the pump until either the sensor detects water, or a pre-set time elapses, depending on which event occurs first. Preferably, the system should automatically detect failure and fouling of the solids sensor.

The capacity of the desludging pump is chosen to be about three times greater than the average production rate of the sludge, and the pump start and stop times set so that the pump can run for up to, say, 50% of the time. The running time of the pump is then trimmed by the control system to keep the blanket height constant.

The sensor has to be cleaned frequently and re-calibrated to trigger at a solids concentration of about 10 kg SS/m^3. When calibrated for this concentration, the sensor will differentiate between the top-water and the sludge blanket.

Recycling top-water will not, in most cases, impose a significant load on the main treatment processes, provided that the consolidation tank is soundly designed and the sludge is not septic. Generally, the load of any pollutant in the top-water will not exceed by more than 5% the load of the pollutant in the sewage. Table 15 lists the typical composition of top-water for different types of sludge.

Table 15. Typical Composition of Top-Water

Type of sludge	BOD (mg/l)	SS (mg/l)	Amm. N (mg/l)
Primary, primary + humus	250–500	500–1000	50–100
Primary + activated	500–2500	1000–5000	50–200
Activated, humus	100–250	250–500	10–50

Consolidation of primary and activated sludges. Special consideration has to be given to the consolidation of mixtures of primary and activated sludge. These have a comparatively high biological activity because of the presence of facultative bacteria in the secondary sludge and substrate in the primary sludge. The performance of the process with such mixtures can therefore be limited and the top-water can be heavily contaminated. The problem seems to be exacerbated in large continuous consolidation tanks, probably because the solids retention time in these tanks can be prolonged, allowing the solids to undergo a high degree of degradation. In view of this, it is expedient to thicken primary and secondary sludges separately. If continuous co-consolidation is preferred, the process should be confined to the wells of primary sedimentation tanks and consolidation tanks up to about 8 m in diameter.

Where an activated sludge from a nitrifying plant is to be consolidated, it should be taken from a position on the plant where the concentration of nitrate nitrogen is comparatively low in order to reduce the risk of denitrification. The best position is a short distance downstream from the anoxic zone, where the concentration of nitrate nitrogen is low but the liquor has received some aeration.

Where the treatment works serves a population of more than about 10 000, it is probably more cost effective to thicken the activated sludge mechanically with, for example, a gravity belt press or centrifuge rather than by consolidation. Any additional cost associated with producing a thicker sludge in such machines will be offset by savings in the subsequent treatment and disposal.

Consolidation of digested sludge. Approximately 50% of sludge in the UK is digested, and most of this is disposed of to land, very often without any substantial thickening. Digested sludges have poor intrinsic consolidation properties, at least a factor of 10 lower than primary sludges. Also, fresh digested sludge contains bubbles of biogas which have to be expelled before consolidation can proceed. Special processes may have to be used.

The most common process is to batch consolidate the sludge for 2–3 months in tanks or lagoons about 1 m deep. The long retention provides time for the biological activity to subside, and the shallow depth of sludge helps bubbles to escape and consolidation to proceed. Thickened sludges with dry-solids concentrations up to about 5–6% DS are obtained.

If the digestion process proceeds to near completion in the primary digester, water separation is possible in the storage tanks if they are equipped with mixers to enable cooling and release of biogas. After settlement, water can be decanted from the surface.

In a comprehensive paper presented in 1971, Brown *et al*[12] described experiments to thicken digested sludge from Beckton and Crossness sewage works (a) in shallow beds, (b) in large tanks, (c) with aeration followed by settlement, and (d) with flocculating agents. It was found that the volume of sludge could be reduced by one-third within 5 days by storage and decanting in shallow beds with a depth of 0.3 m. Although slightly less effective, deeper beds also yielded substantial reductions. Many works have adopted the process, but it requires a large area and is labour intensive.

In the experiments with aeration and settlement, it was found that 40% of the original volume could be separated after only 2–3 days' settlement. This earlier work was continued in the early 1980s by Hurley *et al*[13] who found that pre-aeration of digested sludge prior to consolidation improves the rate of consolidation by at least a factor of 5. In open-topped storage tanks, several aeration devices were tested including coarse bubble grids, venturi aerators and submerged turbines. In pilot-scale experiments carried out at Penybont sewage-treatment works in 1993[14], results similar to the earlier work were obtained. However, it was noted that digestion resumed rapidly after aeration, thus impeding consolidation. Optimum conditions varied with the type and intensity of aeration.

Aeration strips the sludge of micro-bubbles, inhibits further production of methane and carbon dioxide, and raises the pH to above 8 by removing carbon dioxide from solution. Patents for the 'AERCON' process (as it is termed) are owned by Thames Water.

Elutriation has been used successfully at Burton-on-Trent and Mansfield sewage-treatment works. This process involves mixing the digested sludge with 2–3 parts of final effluent and then consolidating the mixture continuously. The final effluent cools the sludge, reducing the biological activity, and washes out bubbles of biogas. Elutriation has the disadvantage that it washes virtually all the ammoniacal nitrogen from the digested sludge into the top-water, increasing the nitrogen loading on secondary treatment.

Consolidating digested sludge is not necessarily cost effective. At some treatment works, especially new ones, it may be more effective to thicken the raw sludge, making thickening of the digested sludge unnecessary.

3.3 Gravity Belt Thickener

The gravity belt thickener (Fig. 8 and Plate 2) was commercially developed during the early 1970s as a result of the success of the filter belt press and the widespread use of the activated-sludge process. Although developed for activated sludge, the gravity belt thickener has since proved to be a cost-effective alternative for thickening all types of sewage sludge as well as a variety of inorganic sludges.

The gravity belt thickener consists of an endless filter belt on which thickening takes place in three phases: conditioning, gravity drainage and compression. Flocculated sludge is fed onto the belt and, as it moves along, water passes through the weave of the belt. At the discharge end of the machine, the sludge is further thickened by the compression caused by it being turned over onto itself. The belt is continuously washed by a high-pressure wash station.

Gravity belt thickeners are used for all types of sewage sludge, although they are at their most economical when handling sludge of less than 1% DS feed, and thickening to 6% DS.

Standard designs are available in 1.0, 1.5 and 2.0 m effective widths, with flow

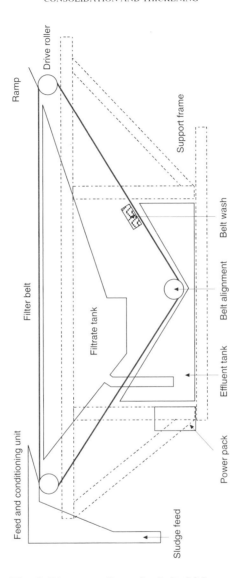

Fig. 8. Diagram of gravity belt thickener

rates from as low as 10 m³/h. A throughput of up to 75 m³/m width per hour can be achieved with some activated sludges, but it is often at the expense of lower performance and increased consumption of polyelectrolyte.

Primary sludge can be thickened to 10% DS at which point it is difficult to process further without expensive pumping systems. Activated sludge is normally thickened to 5% DS.

Plate 2. Aquabelt installation

3.3.1 Process design. *Conditioning.* Sludge thickening with a gravity belt thickener is made possible by the addition of polyelectrolyte to the sludge. The polyelectrolyte adheres to the sludge particles, causing the release of surface water, neutralization of charge, and the conglomeration of small particles by means of bridging. The result of this is flocculation of the sludge solids. The process of conditioning sewage sludge is dealt with in detail in the companion handbook *Sewage Sludge: Dewatering, Drying and Incineration.*

In order to achieve effective flocculation, it is necessary to control (a) the energy used for mixing the sludge and polyelectrolyte together, (b) the flocculating conditions, and (c) the time. This is achieved by the use of a non-clogging, variable-orifice in-line mixer, used in conjunction with a non-turbulent flocculation cylinder positioned immediately upstream from the gravity belt thickener.

Gravity drainage. After conditioning, the sludge is passed down a gently sloping chute onto the filter belt. The loose water separates rapidly from the sludge and passes through the belt weave. Ploughs gently turn the sludge over, allowing more water to pass through the filter media.

Compression. By the time the sludge reaches the compression stage, it has lost over 80% of its water. At the end of the horizontal travel the sludge encounters a ramp where it is turned over on itself several times before being thrust over the edge into a collecting tank. Any remaining sludge deposits clinging to the filter belt are removed by a plastic scraper blade.

3.3.2 Mechanical design. *Framework.* The frame is a semi-rigid, self-contained design, so that the free-standing frame holds the press parts together but relies upon a rigid foundation to hold the machine level. Coated mild steel is sufficient for all applications as the frame is not in continual contact with the sludge or filtrate.

Rollers and bearings. The fabricated rollers hold and guide the belt. They are manufactured with stub-end shafts, and designed to withstand the imposed loading.

As the roller deflects, it imposes side thrust, and therefore selection of the bearings becomes important to the long-term maintenance costs. As a minimum, bearings should be of the taper-lock, collar-mounted, spherical-roller type, designed for a life of 100 000 h. The bearing housing should be of the split-case type and dowelled into position, again minimizing maintenance costs.

Filter belts. The range of filter belts is extensive, and it is possible to have a different type of belt for each specific application; however, within the industry it is possible to standardize on one or two types. They are made from woven polyester and are available in standard widths cut to length, and joined by a stainless-steel clipper seam which allows rapid replacement. Under normal conditions, belts have a life of two years.

Belt washing. To ensure efficient operation, the belt is washed continuously in a separate high-pressure wash station using final effluent. The spray stations are totally enclosed to eliminate aerosol mists, with the belt entrance and exit points protected by easily replaceable rubber seals. As a general rule, the volume of washwater required is 5 m^3/m belt width per hour at a pressure of 6 bar. Reduced volumes and pressures of wash water result in inadequate cleaning of the belt, and subsequent blinding and fall-off in performance.

Belt tensioning and steering. The gravity belt thickener is provided with a fully automatic belt tensioning and steering alignment system, self-contained with all necessary pumps, reservoirs, piping and controls. Automatic sensing devices actuate the belt tracking system and ensure alignment of the belt, and limit switches on each side of the belt detect any malfunction of the tracking system.

3.3.3 Operation. *Start-up.* The start-up sequence may be commenced from a single button, the sequence being controlled by a programmable logic controller (PLC) in the control panel. The usual sequence is (a) filter belt drive; (b) filter belt wash pump; (c) polyelectrolyte pump; (d) sludge feed pump; and (e) thickened sludge pump.

When closing down the plant, the feed and polyelectrolyte pumps are stopped, but the belt and wash pump continue for a period to ensure that the belt is shut down in a clean condition. The thickened sludge pump will continue to operate until a low-level probe in the sump is reached.

Routine operation. If the dry-solids content of the feed sludge is consistent after initial setting up, the machine may be left unattended for long periods. If the dry-solids concentration of the incoming sludge changes, the position of the thickened sludge (relative to the ramp) is monitored with level probes and the speed of the sludge pump is automatically controlled, whilst keeping the polyelectrolyte pump speed constant.

Optimum operating conditions are normally established during commissioning, and only minor adjustments need to be made to compensate for variations in sludge quality. The operator can observe the effect of any adjustments and then rapidly re-establish optimum conditions.

Normally, the only control tests required are for the dry-solids content of the feed sludge, the thickened sludge, and the SS concentration in the filtrate. Combining these data with the amount of polyelectrolyte used, the overall plant efficiency may be calculated in terms of percent solids capture and kilograms of polymer consumed per tonne of dry solids processed.

Nature of feed sludge. Different types of sludge vary in their amenability to thickening, and gravity belt thickeners are normally best suited to dealing with very thin sludge. A fresh sludge is more amenable to thickening, whilst an older sludge requires a higher dose of polyelectrolyte to achieve the same result.

Polyelectrolyte dosage. If insufficient polyelectrolyte is used, the flocculation will be incomplete and there will be insufficient flocs to allow free drainage and obtain a clear filtrate. Conversely, the use of excessive polyelectrolyte must be avoided as it may lead to blinding of the filter belt.

The choice of polyelectrolyte is very important, since significant differences in performance can be achieved with the same sludge using different grades of polyelectrolytes.

The mixer setting will have a significant effect on the efficiency of flocculation and hence the overall polyelectrolyte consumption. The energy which is necessary to flocculate each type of sludge will vary; too much energy will shear the delicate activated sludge flocs, whilst the more robust co-settled sludge needs a greater input of energy before they begin to flocculate.

Belt speed. The throughput of sludge is normally related to the speed of the belt. At higher speeds, greater solids throughput is achieved but at the expense of thickened sludge dry solids. Lower belt speeds can produce much higher dry-solids, but with a reduced overall solids throughput. Thus any setting of the belt speed is a compromise, depending on local requirements.

Performance. Table 16 shows typical results from a variety of site trials and full-scale installations.

Table 16. Typical Performance of Gravity Belt Thickeners

Sludge	Feed (%DS)	Thickened (%DS)	Filtrate (mg/l SS)
Surplus activated	0.4	6.6	81
Oxidation ditch	0.6	7.2	78
Co-settled	2.9	8.5	220
Digested	2.4	9.3	316

3.4 Centrifuge

A centrifuge (Plate 3) is a mechanical device which employs centrifugal forces to enhance the settling rate of particles. Light particles are discharged with the centrate and heavy particles pass to the thickening zone and are discharged as thickened sludge. The process is also used for dewatering (as opposed to thickening) sewage sludge, and is described in more detail in the companion handbook *Sewage Sludge: Dewatering, Drying, and Incineration.* The centrifuge has a very small footprint, and can be installed in the open, provided that there is suitable pipework lagging for the winter.

3.4.1 Construction. There are several types of centrifuge, but for dealing with sewage sludge the decanter type with solid bowl and scroll is invariably supplied. The decanter centrifuge is a conical, cylindrical rotor containing a screw conveyor

Plate 3. Centrifuge installation

(scroll). The most common material of construction for both the bowl and conveyor is stainless steel, although carbon steel is used when the capital cost is more important than maintenance costs.

One end of the bowl tapers to form the beach up which the cake is scrolled prior to discharge, and the clarified liquor decants over adjustable weirs at the other end of the bowl.

Both the bowl and the screw rotate at high speed in the same direction, but the speed of the screw is a few revolutions per minute lower, and it therefore has the effect of a conveyor. The differential between bowl and conveyor is provided through the gearbox mounted at one end of the bowl, and can be varied by a variable-speed brake attached to the pinion shaft of the gearbox.

The conveyor fits inside the bowl with a radial clearance of 1–2 mm. It rotates relative to the bowl from a fraction of 1 rev/min up to, say, 30 rev/min faster or slower, to convey the solids to the discharge ports.

The centrifuge is increasingly equipped with instrumentation such as flow meters, vibration monitors, feed solids meters, centrate quality controllers, etc., and some manufacturers offer complete systems with intelligent control to optimize dryness, solids recovery, capacity and even the economic efficiency of the centrifuge plant.

3.4.2 Conditioning. The quality of the final product depends on the settling characteristics of the activated sludge and the effectiveness of polymer dosing. Activated sludge is almost always conditioned with a cationic polyelectrolyte added to the sludge immediately upstream from the centrifuge. It is possible to produce a reasonable product without the addition of polymers, but conditioning enables maximum performance with good solids recovery.

3.4.3 Performance. It is usual to measure feed and polymer rate, and to analyse the total solids content of feed and cake, and the suspended solids in the centrate. The polymer solids content will be known from the plant settings. The differences between suspended solids and total solids in the feed, and particularly the cake, are negligible for the calculation accuracy required. From these analyses, solids recovery and polymer dosage are calculated, and sometimes the centrate volume rate is also calculated.

A decanter centrifuge can thicken a well-treated secondary sludge without the need for flocculants, recovering 85% to over 90% of the feed solids. With a small amount of flocculant, over 99% can be recovered and the thickened sludge contains 5–7% DS.

3.5 Dissolved-Air Flotation

The technique of air flotation can be used when the solid particles have a low rate of settlement, and in sewage treatment the process is used to thicken surplus activated sludge.

The specific gravity of fine suspended solids is lowered by the attachment of micro-bubbles and buoyed to the surface. Its application in sewage sludge treatment involves dissolving air under pressure and subsequently releasing the pressure in the flotation vessel.

The earliest attempts at sludge thickening by flotation relied on natural gas evolution or gases evolved by electrolysis, or adding chemicals. These processes were not economically viable and were successful only with primary sludge, which in any case could be thickened adequately by gravity. However, surplus activated sludge is difficult to concentrate by gravity alone, and flotation thickening is sometimes used.

3.5.1 Operation. Dissolved-air flotation is carried out by releasing the pressure on a saturated liquid so that micro-bubbles between 40 and 60 microns in diameter are formed (Fig. 9). These attach themselves to sludge particles and carry them to the surface of the tank, forming a float of thickened sludge.

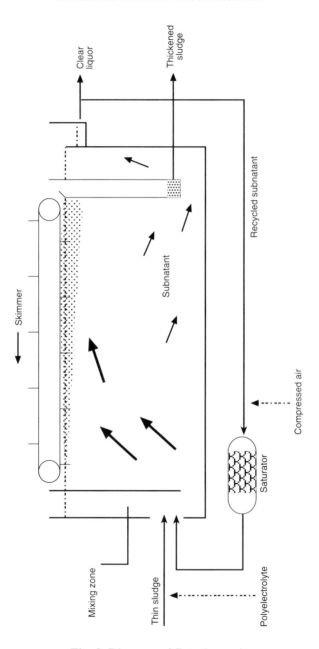

Fig. 9. Diagram of flotation unit

A polyelectrolyte is invariably used in the UK to promote the separation and achieve maximum solids capture. Polyelectrolyte is added to the sludge or to the saturated liquor immediately upstream from the flotation tank, and the sludge and saturated liquid are introduced together in the inlet zone of the tank.

At the surface the float rises above the water level and surplus water drains through the layer which, to allow this, should be no more than 500–600 mm thick. Thickened sludge is removed continuously or intermittently by a scraper. The method of operation of the scraper affects the quality of the thickened sludge, and they may be fitted with a variable-speed drive or simple timers.

The clear subnatant effluent is recycled and saturated with air in a pressure vessel. Sometimes this is packed with pall rings to encourage complete mixing and saturation, but there is then a possibility that deposition of sludge solids may eventually cause a blockage. The excess liquid is returned to the inlet of the sewage-treatment works.

3.5.2 Performance. Surplus activated sludge is thickened from 0.5–4.0% DS using a polyelectrolyte. There is little performance data from the UK, but at Aycliffe[15] surplus activated sludge containing 5000 mg/l SS was thickened to produce a sludge containing 4% DS using a loading of 9.75 kg/m^2. h. The process is reliable and has a good solids capture, but has high maintenance and power costs.

Activated sludge may be thickened without prior conditioning, but it requires larger plant size, and the solids recovery is poor.

4. Sludge Pumping

4.1 Introduction

The transfer of sewage sludge plays an integral part in the day-to-day running of a sewage-treatment works, and most unit processes within the works depend on the reliability of the pumping equipment serving them. Pump failure due to inappropriate selection, operation and maintenance can lead to a failed discharge consent within hours.

The range of pumps from which the designer can select is extensive; it should be possible to choose a pump which is suited to each individual application. In sludge pumping applications it is considered that absolute efficiency should not be the sole criterion for selecting pumps. Consideration should also be given to factors such as the nature of the sludge, the degree of contamination, and the overall running and maintenance costs.

Sludge can differ widely in consistency depending upon (a) the treatment process, (b) the effectiveness of pretreatment, and (c) the quantity of rags, grit and other solids. The sludge will often exhibit characteristics which are particular to an area or region; for example, in a carpet or textile manufacturing area a significant amount of stringy material may be present. The quantity of grit may also vary due to geographical location and the type and length of the sewerage system.

The consistency of the sludge influences the pumping resistance, and the characteristics (such as screenings and grit content) will affect the operation and maintenance requirements of the system.

Due to the large differences in sludge encountered in sewage treatment, it is important to be able to identify the common characteristics of sludge used in the design of pumping installations. A summary of expected sludge concentrations is presented in Table 17.

The trend towards the production of thicker, drier sludge has resulted in the development of pumps which are capable of handling cake-like materials up to a consistency of 65% DS.

Table 17. Concentrations of Sludge

Type of sludge	Range %DS	Typical %DS
Primary settling tank		
Primary sludge	3–8	5.0
Primary and surplus activated sludge	3–7	4.0
Primary and humus sludge	1–7	5.0
Scum	2–5	3.0
Secondary settling tank		
Surplus activated sludge	0.25–1.5	0.75
Humus sludge	1–3	1.5
Gravity thickener		
Primary sludge only	5–10	8.0
Primary and surplus activated sludge	3–8	4.0
Primary and humus sludge	4–10	5.0
Belt thickener		
Surplus activated sludge	3–5	4.0
Centrifuge	15–35	28.0
Filterbelt press	20–35	30.0
Plate and frame filter press	30–45	37.0

Basic pumping systems comprise an arrangement of suction and delivery pipework, pump and driver, non-return valves and, ideally, isolating valves. The pump and system characteristics should be compatible.

The system characteristics are determined from an analysis of the sludge type (e.g. consistency, rag content) and the required pump duty (e.g. pump capacity, frequency, static and friction head, form of control). Pump characteristics vary widely depending upon the type of pump; those used for pumping sewage sludge are normally either of the rotor dynamic or the positive-displacement type.

4.2 Theory of Sludge Pumping

The flow of sewage sludge, as with water, is subject to laminar and turbulent flow.

However, the well-established Newtonian flow equations which apply to water do not apply to the flow of sludge. The effective viscosity varies with the flow condition, and as such may be higher at the pipe entry than at the pipe discharge point. The transition between laminar and turbulent flow is not as clearly defined as for a Newtonian fluid. Instead, a transition zone exists where flow is part laminar and part turbulent.

The degree of resistance to flow (head-loss) generated by the movement of sludge in a pipeline will vary appreciably for different types of sludge. The resistance to flow of sewage sludge has been the subject of many papers: Ackers and Allen[16] reported on tests carried out on sludge at Oldham, Bury, Rochdale and Bolton for the North West Water Authority. Typical head-loss/flow curves are shown in Fig. 10, from which can be seen the variation in head-losses for apparently similar sludges.

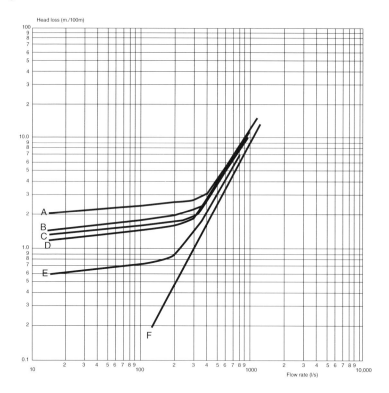

Fig. 10. Typical sludge characteristics

For the design of simple sludge pumping installations it is necessary to predict the maximum head-loss and flow rate for the worst case, as this will determine the type and capacity of the pump and the power requirement. The pump must be selected to convey the sludge at a convenient operating velocity. Operating towards the laminar zone will increase the tendency for blockage to occur, whereas operating well towards the turbulent zone will induce high head-losses which may cause pumping to be impracticable and uneconomic.

Ackers and Allen[16] suggest that the system is designed to operate at the 'transition point' or 'intersection velocity' for the thickest sludge to be conveyed. The true intersection velocity for a particular sludge can only be determined from an analysis of the rheological properties of the sludge in question, but is generally in the region of 2–3 m/s.

Calculation of the estimated maximum head-loss for this operating velocity is then carried out using the Colebrook-White equation[17] to define the initial value (using appropriate Ks and viscosity values). The initial value is then factored by a head-loss ratio (HLR) to determine the predicted head-loss for the thickest sludge to be conveyed. For design at the intersection velocity, Ackers and Allen suggest that a conservative value for the HLR of 1.75 is appropriate for general purposes.

4.3 Rotor Dynamic Pumps

Rotor dynamic pumps are perhaps the most widely used, being of simple design and producing an even delivery. There are three main forms of rotor dynamic pumps which can be considered for use with sewage sludge.

The impeller design characterizes each pump and determines its application for a particular duty. Clearances should be generous and the impellers open-bladed with back-shrouded blades to keep grit away from the glands. To minimize blockages due to rags and stringy materials, leading edges should be kept to a minimum, and thickened and profiled to inhibit the clinging of such fibres.

Rotor dynamic pumps can be arranged for wet- or dry-well installations mounted either vertically or horizontally, submersibly or immersibly. Typical installation details are shown in Fig. 11. They can be designed to pass solids up to the suction branch diameter, but normally the maximum size is a 100 mm sphere. They can operate against a closed valve but are not self-priming.

4.3.1 Radial (centrifugal) flow pump. There are four main types of centrifugal impeller which are suitable for pumping sludge, although there are many variations.

Single-vane impeller. The impeller (Fig. 12) is designed to avoid the plaiting of

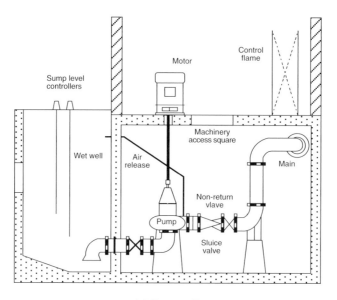

(a) Dry well

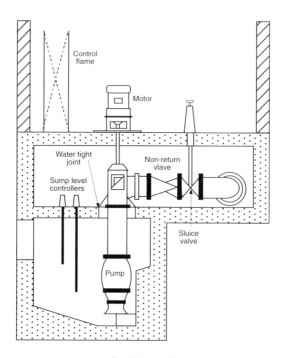

(b) Wet well

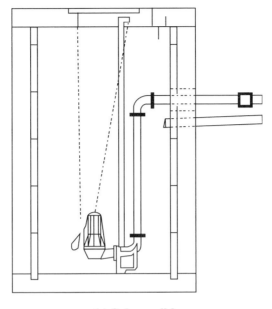

(c) Submersible

Fig. 11. Typical layout of dry and wet-well installations

long fibrous constituents in the sludge and is suited to the pumping of raw sludge. It is capable of handling sludge up to approximately 6% DS, but both head/capacity and efficiency are significantly de-rated at the higher solids limit.

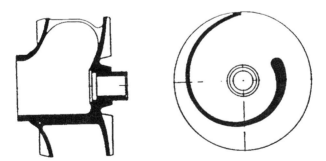

Fig.12. Single-vane impeller

Free-flow (vortex) impeller. In this arrangement the impeller (Fig. 13) has shallow blades set back into the drive side of the pump casing, creating a forced vortex spiral flow through the pump which drives the liquid across the face of the impeller. This gives an uninterrupted passage for the sewage flow, reducing the incidence of clogging. It is claimed to be quieter in operation with less vibration than the conventional impeller, with subsequent increased wear resistance and improved reliability.

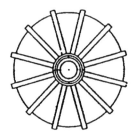

Fig. 13. Free-flow impeller

It is recommended for use with sludge where liberation of gas can affect performance, such as thickened raw and digested sludge. It can handle sludge up to 8% DS but at a significantly reduced efficiency.

Twin-channel and three-channel impellers. The twin- and three-channel impellers (Fig. 14) have a smaller free passage cross-section than the single-vane impeller, and higher efficiencies can be achieved. However, their application is limited to non-gassing mixtures which do not contain fibrous solids, and with dry-solid concentrations in the region of 2–3%.

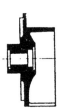

Fig. 14. Twin- and three-channel impeller

4.3.2 Mixed-flow pump. For larger quantities and lower heads the mixed-flow pump is available. The flow through the impeller has both an axial and radial component, and the component proportions are specified by the pump designer to obtain the desired pump output characteristics. Care has to be taken in the specification and design for sewage duties to avoid choking and blockage with stringy materials in the sewage. If too great an axial component is included with resultant smaller passages, the leading edges of the impeller will collect rags and stringy material.

These pumps are often used for handling large quantities on applications with storm sewage and can be either of the volute-casing type, similar in appearance to the centrifugal pump, or of the suspended-bowl type.

4.3.3 Axial-flow pump. In the axial-flow pump the flow through the impeller is all axial and the pump casing is of the bowl type with guide vanes. The passages through the blades are relatively small and the leading edges are prone to picking up stringy material, which makes the pump unsuitable for handling large solids or fibrous materials. However, in certain cases, where the total head is low, axial-flow pumps are used for pumping activated and digested sludge which is free from clogging material.

4.3.4 Semi-axial solids handling. This pump incorporates a hybrid design of the screw type (positive displacement) and centrifugal impeller arrangement, consisting of a single blade extending axially towards the suction inlet.

The first portion of the blade provides a positive-displacement action, acting like an Archimedean screw, and the outlet portion acts like a centrifugal pump to develop the pressure. An example of such an arrangement is shown in Fig. 15.

The pump is suited to lifting much thicker sludge than conventional centrifugal pumps, with a dry-solids content up to 15% claimed by manufacturers. The suction and discharge condition should be considered when evaluating such claims. Due to the screw action of the impeller, it is possible to handle fibrous and gaseous sludge. The efficiency is also quoted as being far superior, with energy savings given as 5–20% when compared to a single-channel impeller and 50–60% against a vortex impeller.

The provision of a pre-rotation chamber to induce a vortex around the pump suction inlet allows a single screw centrifugal pump to provide a continuously variable output to match varying inflow rates. In this manner, variable output is achieved without the degree of sophistication (and hence extra cost) needed for variable- speed control, allowing continuous transfer of sludge to occur throughout the loading cycle.

4.4 Positive-Displacement Pumps

The positive-displacement pump operates on the principle of positive encapsulation

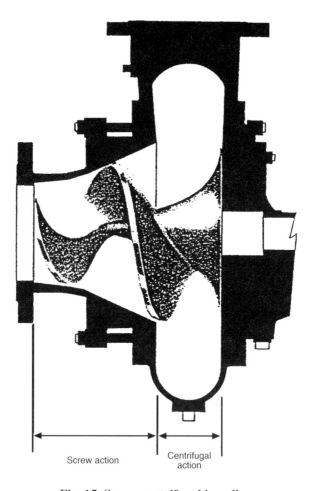

Screw action

Centrifugal action

Fig. 15. Screw centrifugal impeller

and subsequent transfer of an element of fluid. They are ideally suited to pumping sludge containing a high concentration of dry solids over relatively long distances, or for liquids which are not free-flowing, the principal requirement being that liquid must be able to be induced into the pump.

In general they should not be operated against a closed valve, since they are normally driven through a large mechanical reduction which gives large torques and, in consequence, very high pressures due to the incompressibility of liquids. It is normal to install pressure-relief valves in the delivery connections to prevent mechanical damage. Upon initial priming, a number of positive-displacement pumps offer high suction lifts often approaching full vacuum head.

They have a characteristic in which the head is independent of speed, and capacity is approximately proportional to speed. These characteristics are shown in Fig. 16.

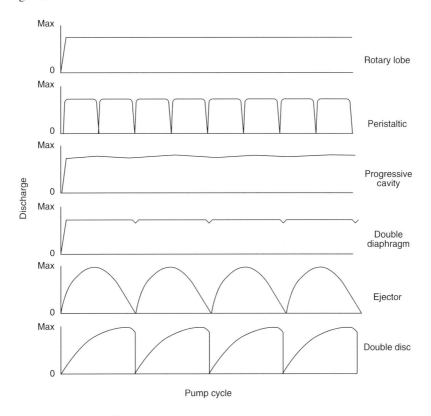

Fig. 16. Characteristics of positive-displacement pumps

Positive-displacement pumps which are suitable for pumping sewage sludge are available in many forms, and the principal types are described below.

4.4.1 Piston pump. Piston pumps are capable of delivering sludge containing a high concentration of solids at moderate flows against very high heads, and the pneumatically activated type is able to deliver at outputs of up to 150 bar and up to 110 m^3/h. They are reported to be capable of pumping sludge-cake with a dry-solids content of up to 50% and can handle highly abrasive and high-volume solids.

Piston pumps of the reciprocating type driven through a crankshaft have a constant output which can only be varied by changing the crankshaft speed, or the

length of the stroke if eccentrics are utilized. They cannot be operated against a closed valve, and safety or pressure-relief valves should always be installed to prevent damage and guard against excess pressures.

Hydraulically or pneumatically actuated piston pumps have a variable output controlled by the pressure and flows of the hydraulic oil or compressed air. They can be operated against a closed valve, provided that the system can withstand the pressure which is generated. Dry running is not advised.

Pistons are made of various materials including cast iron, cast steel, ceramics and elastomers, and operate in cast-steel or stainless steel-liners. Glands are provided to prevent the escape of pumped liquid around the piston. The level of maintenance varies widely, depending on the characteristics of the sludge, operating time, and non-use periods.

Special inlet feed arrangements are required for pumping sludge in excess of 20% DS. The thickened sludge is conveyed from the feed hopper by means of the intermeshing augers in the force-feed device. This device pressurizes the sludge in the pump hopper, thus assisting in the charging of the pumping cylinders and improving filling efficiency. The use of intermeshing flights on the auger prevents a build-up of sticky material on the shafts.

The main application of the piston pump is for sludge transfer duties. The pumping pressure applied to the sludge causes a fraction of the water to migrate to the pipe wall to form a lubricating layer. The pumping of very dry sludge which does not lubricate the pipe wall is aided by the injection of small quantities of liquid. The hydraulically actuated type has the additional capability of charging filter presses and, if power is available, both types can be used for clearing blockages in pipe systems.

4.4.2 Diaphragm pump. The diaphragm pump is useful in the medium-head range and has the advantage that there are no sliding metallic parts exposed to abrasive media. It has the disadvantage that the diaphragm can easily be ruptured by over-pressure or sharp objects in the sludge. The diaphragm pump is fundamentally similar to a piston pump but with the piston being replaced by a flexible diaphragm actuated in a reciprocating motion from a rotating crankshaft. Alternatively a chamber behind the diaphragm can be charged and exhausted hydraulically or pneumatically. A typical arrangement is shown in Fig. 17.

Suction and delivery non-return valves are required in a similar manner as for the piston pump. They are normally of the ball or flexible flap type.

Characteristically, these are similar to the piston pump but operate in the lower

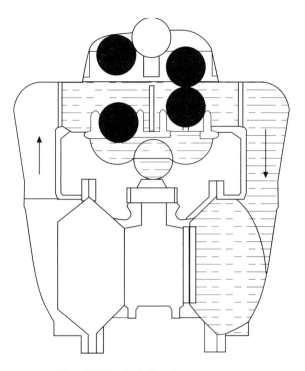

Fig. 17. Typical diaphragm pump

pressure ranges. Mechanically actuated diaphragms must not be operated against closed valve conditions, otherwise rupture of the diaphragm will occur. Hydraulically and pneumatically operated diaphragms can be operated against closed valves without damage, since the pressure is balanced across the diaphragm. Dry running is permissible for diaphragm pumps.

Diaphragm pumps are self-sealing, containing the liquor within the pump without resorting to glands. However, the diaphragms are vulnerable to puncture by sharp objects, or over-exposure on mechanically actuated units.

The main applications are for sludge withdrawal duties, short distance sludge transfer and, for hydraulically actuated units, the charging of filter presses.

4.4.3 Disc pump. Disc pumps are available in single and double-disc versions. They are suited for low to medium transfer duties handling sludge containing grit, solids and rags. The single-disc type is not self-priming and requires a non-return valve on the suction line. Double-disc pumps are capable of running dry and are self-priming.

Disc pumps are often confused with diaphragm pumps, but in reality they are quite different; the discs operate as pistons and non-return valves, with a separate seal being required to prevent the escape of pumped media. For double-disc pumps, the basis of operation is two discs enclosed in a common chamber, one closing the inlet port and the other the outlet port.

Tough rubber discs reciprocate in opposition to each other: when moving apart suction is created, and when they move together pressure is generated. The discs seat according to their position relative to the stroke movement, and the general arrangement of such a pump is shown in Fig. 18.

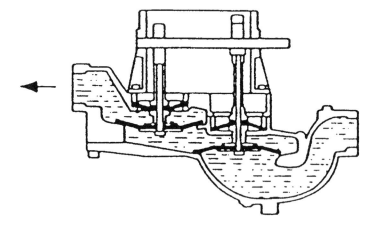

Fig. 18. Double-disc pump

A seal is required to prevent leakage past the rods which operate the discs but, because of the relatively short disc movement, flexible trunnion seals are adopted which eliminate a point of wear and leakage problems.

The pumps have a pulsating output, the non-return valves are inherent mechanically actuated features of the design and, apart from the discs, there are no parts to wear. They should not be operated against a closed valve since the basic operation is one of positive displacement; the output varies according to the suction condition. Disc pumps are used for desludging primary and secondary settlement tanks and also for low-head, low-quantity transfer duties.

4.4.4 Ejector pump. The hydraulic ram, more commonly known as an ejector, works on the simple principle of allowing the liquid to be pumped to gravitate into a vessel through a non-return valve. As the liquid level rises in the vessel, a float operates an air-valve, admitting compressed air under force which blows the liquid out through another non-return valve into the rising main. The float then re-sets, closing the air inlet valve, and operates a second air-valve which releases the pressure, allowing the compressed air in the vessel to be discharged. The cycle repeats after the chamber has filled, and the cycle time can be extended by incorporating a timer to inhibit the operation of the air-admission valve.

An ejector has no moving parts, other than non-return valves, and is glandless. It has a pulsed output relating to the cycle time, with each discharge pulse having a capacity equal to the volume of the chamber (which is typically 300 l). Like hydraulically and pneumatically operated piston and discharge pumps, they can be operated against a closed valve condition.

Although not widely used for sewage sludge applications, the ejector may be used for desludging primary or secondary tanks when the chambers can be arranged for self-flooding, and operate in conjunction with a cycle timer to transfer sludge over medium distances against moderate heads. They are maintenance-free but relatively expensive, and require more space than the alternatives.

4.4.5 Peristaltic pump. The peristaltic (or tube) pump is best known as a metering or sample pump, and has been developed over the past fifty years. More recently, with the advancement of reinforced flexible-tube technology, designs incorporating up to 100 mm diameter tube have been developed and, in consequence, the pump has found an application in pumping sewage sludge.

The principle of operation (Fig. 19) comprises a series of concentric rotating rollers within an annular chamber in which a tube is fitted. The tube follows a continual cycle of occlusion and restitution, causing the pumped liquid to be drawn into the tube and discharged at the delivery end. An added feature, which is available on some models, is the ability to operate in reverse, in order to clear blockages in the suction line.

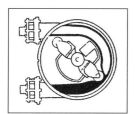 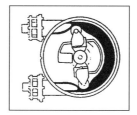 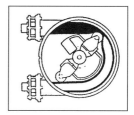

Fig. 19. Principle of operation of peristaltic pump

Peristaltic pumps are glandless and inherently self-priming, and can run dry,

having an output which is independent of head conditions. There are no contact components and the sludge passes through the hose with no vanes, valves or other obstructions, giving the pump the ability to handle fibrous and rag-type material, with a reduced risk of blockage. They should not be operated in a closed-valve situation. Due to the continual flexing of the tube, they have a finite life which can be 3000 h, depending upon the liquid being pumped and the rate and pressure of pumping. The output fluctuates according to the number of occlusion rollers. Apart from the planned replacement of the tube, maintenance of peristaltic pumps is minimal.

Peristaltic pumps are suitable for pumping sludge and grit, dewatering primary and secondary settlement tanks, thickened digester feed sludge and low-capacity medium-head transfer duties.

4.4.6 Rotary lobe pump. The rotary lobe pump is a rotary positive-displacement unit in which two lobe rotors counter-rotate within a chamber, producing a pumping action. The two rotors are synchronized and driven through a gearbox which ensures that they do not come into contact, but operate with close clearance, and this feature enables the pump to run dry. However, because the lobes are driven through shafts, seals are necessary to prevent leakage. The principle of operation of a two-lobe pump is shown in Fig. 20.

The rotary action of positive-displacement (ie. non-reciprocating) pumps provides an inherent non-return feature of the pump and, provided that reverse rotation does not occur, non-return valves are not required. The rotary action also produces a relatively smooth discharge.

The pump casings are normally made of ductile iron and fitted with an easily removable front cover to facilitate maintenance. Rotary lobes for sewage duties are often made of urethane or rubber. If grit is pumped, urethane rotors are normally adopted with the clearances adjusted accordingly; and if good suction performance is required, rubber lobes are fitted and arranged to have a rolling contact.

The output of the pumps is proportional to the speed of rotor rotation; and, for longer life, lower speeds are to be preferred. The pumps are not suitable for operation against a closed valve. Because of the smooth rounded contours of the lobes and pump chamber, they have the ability to pump rags, although stringy material can cause problems.

Rotary lobe pumps are used for the transfer of sewage sludge over medium distances at moderate rates. They are also used for desludging primary and secondary settlement tanks, feeding digesters and belt presses. They are suited to

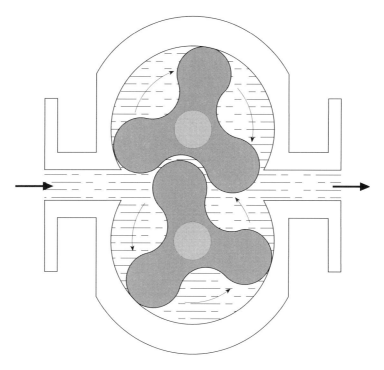

Fig. 20. Rotary lobe pump

high-capacity medium-head transfer duties.

4.4.7 Progressive cavity pump. The helical rotor pump, of which the Mono pump is an example, comprises a resilient stator having a double internal helix (made of rubber or other resilient material) and a single helical metallic rotor which rotates within the stator with a slightly eccentric motion. The rotors are usually manufactured from nitralloy or hard chrome plated stainless steel.

The rotor is of a constant circular cross section, the centres forming a helix which is eccentric to the rotor axis. The pitch of the stator is twice that of the rotor, and the two engage in such a manner that the rotor section traverses the stator aperture to maintain a positive seal along the length of the stator. The seal effectively progresses continuously through the pump, hence giving the uniform positive displacement. Fig. 21 indicates the rotor in four different positions in the stator.

Whilst this pump has a positive displacement, it is reversible and has a self-priming pumping action coupled with uniform flow pulsations. The output is proportional to the speed, and they cannot be operated against a closed valve;

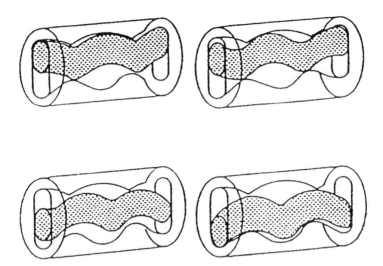

Fig. 21. Principle of progressive cavity pump

neither should they be allowed to run dry, otherwise wear will occur. On high-pressure abrasive and high-viscosity media it is essential that the pump is only operated at low speeds; however, it has the advantage that the stator rotor unit always forms a seal, eliminating the necessity of non-return valves, although they are often incorporated in installations of this type.

These pumps are used for sludge transfer and desludging duties where maintained priming can be assured. For general pumping duties with sludge containing up to 9% DS, the progressive cavity pump generally requires a conventional flanged suction port. It is possible to pump sludge in excess of 9% DS using an open suction port fitted with a rectangular hopper. By using an auger to mechanically feed the sludge, this design has been reported to handle up to 20% DS. Where high-solid slurries or dewatered cake is to be handled, the feed device may be modified by proprietary means (twin augers or rotating 'fingers' in the feed hopper) to enable 40% DS sludge to be transferred.

4.4.8 Screw pump. The screw pump is perhaps the oldest continuous pumping system invented and is in widespread use today. The pump consists of a revolving spiral inclined at 30–38° to the horizontal in a close-fitting open channel or closed tube, and driven by an electric motor through a reduction gearbox. The open screws are manufactured in fabricated steel and the tube is usually made of GRP.

Pumps of this type are suited to high-capacity low-lift installations, although stepped arrangements are possible for moderate lifts at considerable civil-engineering costs. Screw pumps are ideal for pumping liquids containing solids, stringy and other matter, and have the characteristic that their output always matches their input up to the full capacity of the screw. They are widely used to transfer activated and return sludge within sewage-treatment works because of their ability to handle delicate flocs.

Screw pumps are also used to transfer dry sludge cake and sticky sludge, with reduced risk of clogging. They may be mounted horizontally, vertically or inclined, and can be totally enclosed.

4.5 Air-Lift Pumps

The air-lift principle is widely used for inducing liquid flow from a tank into a vertical pipe, and relies upon a dispersion of air bubbles lowering the density of the liquid in the column. The resulting imbalance in forces promotes liquid flow from the tank into the vertical column, thus restoring the equilibrium. Stable flow is achieved when the resulting static and frictional heads in the column equal the force produced by the change in density.

The air-lift pump is very simple and of low cost, particularly if a compressed air or gas supply is available. It has minimal maintenance requirements, no wearing elements immersed in the sludge, and the incidence of blockage is very low. The air-lift pump is widely used for low head/capacity transfer of secondary and primary sludge, particularly in package treatment works, and as the medium for gas recirculation within digesters. The air-lift pump is limited to lifts of less than 3 m, and is sensitive to variations in suction and discharge heads. It is relatively inefficient in terms of power use.

A modification of the air-lift pump is the pneumatic conveyor driven by large capacity compressors. High-velocity airflow pneumatic conveying equipment is suitable for clogging and abrasive non-flowing materials such as rags and grit found in anaerobic sludge digestion tanks.

5. Odour Control

5.1 Introduction

Odours from sludge processes arise from several sources. Odours from raw sludge held in a tank are associated with low gas flows containing high odour concentrations, whereas a high gas flow extracted from a building usually contains low concentrations. It has been estimated that 50% of complaints to sewage-treatment works regarding odour nuisance are related to sludge handling and treatment processes[18]. Most odorous gases are made up of a mixture of compounds of varying dilutions, changing with time and temperature. However, it is usual to use hydrogen sulphide as an indicator because it has a low detection threshold and is easily identified and measured.

In recent years there has been a growing awareness of environmental nuisance, and public concern and complaints of odour from sewage and sludge-treatment works have to be accepted and acted upon. It is not a defence that the sewage works was there long before the planned new housing or commercial development. Part III of the Environmental Protection Act 1990 requires environmental health officers to investigate complaints and take action when a statutory nuisance exists.

The companion handbook *Preliminary Processes*[19] includes a section on septicity in sewers and its control.

5.2 Chemicals Causing Odours

Odours from sewage sludge normally arise as a result of bacterial activity in the sewer or at the sewage-treatment works. Chemicals with the potential to cause odour nuisance are normally already present in the sewage, or formed during the processing or storage of the sludge. Some compounds which are discharged into the sewerage system in industrial effluents may also lead to odour nuisance.

The release of odours to the atmosphere depends on their concentration in the liquor, the surface exposed to the atmosphere, and the turbulence of the flow. Release also depends on pH: in acidic conditions sulphides and organic acids are readily evolved, while in alkaline conditions ammonia and amines are more likely to dominate.

5.2.1 Hydrogen sulphide. Hydrogen sulphide is formed by the action of micro-organisms on sulphates and other sulphur-containing compounds under anaerobic conditions. It may be present in the incoming sewage if the retention period in the sewerage system is long, especially in warm conditions. Boon[20] has described the background and the theoretical concepts. At a sewage works, hydrogen sulphide can be produced in the sludge handling system, primary sedimentation tanks, gravity thickeners and storage tanks. It is readily released to the atmosphere from the sludge, particularly where there is turbulence. It has a very unpleasant odour, associated with rotten eggs, and is detectable by most individuals at a concentration in the range 2–4 parts per billion. It is a potential danger because the sense of smell is quickly lost as the concentration increases, and unconsciousness and death can occur at a concentration from about 300 ppm. It also causes corrosion to concrete and electrical equipment.

5.2.2 Ammonia. Ammonia is normally present in sewage at relatively low concentrations of up to 100 mg/l. Concentrations higher than this are usually due to industrial discharges, and may be caused by the anaerobic breakdown of high protein wastes. It is also produced during sludge treatment under anaerobic conditions by the breakdown of organic-nitrogen compounds, resulting in concentrations in excess of 500 ppm. Its release to the atmosphere depends on the pH and temperature of the sludge. The threshold of detection of ammonia by smell is about 5 ppm, which is similar to the occupational exposure limit (OEL) and means that, if ammonia is present in detectable concentrations, there is a potential safety problem. On its own, ammonia is not normally a cause of odour nuisance from a works treating domestic sewage.

The use of chlorine to oxidize sulphide where ammonia is present can lead to the formation of chloramines, but these are not formed to the same extent when sodium hypochlorite is used.

5.2.3 Amines. Organic compounds which contain an amine group may be present or formed in sludges, and are detectable at very low concentrations. For example, triethylamine is detectable at 0.2 ppb and is the 'fishy' odour occasionally reported.

5.2.4 Mercaptans. Mercaptans (thiols) are organic sulphur compounds with unpleasant odours, detectable at very low concentrations.

5.2.5 Aldehydes, ketones, organic acids, alcohols and esters. This is a wide range of compounds with different degrees of intensity and unpleasantness of odour.

5.2.6 Skatoles and indoles. This group comprises complex organic-nitrogen compounds characteristic of domestic sewage, and these are detected at very low concentrations.

Table 18 is a shortened form of that from the Warren Spring Laboratory[21], and it should be noted that the threshold values given in the literature can vary by several orders of magnitude because of the different types of equipment used and the complexity of the procedures adopted.

Table 18. Odour Threshold Values (ppm)

Compound	Threshold value
Acetic acid	1.0000
Ammonia	46.8000
Butyric acid	0.0010
Carbon tetrachloride	100.0000
Chlorine	0.3140
Dimethylamine	0.0470
Dimethylsulphide	0.0010
Ethyl mercaptan	0.0010
Hydrogen sulphide	0.0005
Methyl mercaptan	0.0021
Skatole	0.2200
Trimethylamine	0.0002

5.3 Assessment of Odour

The chemical composition of an odour can be determined, but the human nose is the most reliable and accurate instrument for measuring odours, and is capable of detecting some compounds below the detection limit of the most sophisticated instruments.

Electronic 'noses' are now being developed[22] which will become extremely useful in odour control. They are based on the changing conductivity of a polymer sensor as it reacts with the odorous compound. The equipment (which is already used in several industrial applications) consists of a head with an array of sensors, a sample vessel, and computer software to give a comprehensive analysis of the odour profile.

Chemical analysis is a very useful tool for mapping the source and extent of hydrogen sulphide, and this technique has been used with great effect by Thames Water to reduce odour nuisance[23]. 'Maps' of concentrations of hydrogen sulphide (Fig. 22) were produced for an area within and around a sewage works using portable electronic equipment. Contour maps of the hydrogen sulphide concentration were drawn to help to identify the position and extent of odour sources, and appropriate remedial work was carried out.

The measurement of quality, strength and detectability of an odour is carried out using an olfactometer, in which an odorous gas is diluted with clean air and presented to a panel of human assessors. The threshold odour number (TON) is the number of volumes of odour-free air diluting one volume of odour sample when the median of a population of assessors can just detect the mixture. Because this value is a ratio of volumes, it is (in theory) dimensionless, but is frequently given the unit 'odour units per cubic metre' (OU/m^3).

The test uses a panel of human assessors, and therefore has been regarded as subjective and, by implication, unreliable and unscientific. However, olfactometry has several important advantages, and a European working group has been established to formalize standards with respect to design of apparatus, technique and treatment of results. A draft European Standard on olfactometry has been compiled[24] which includes sections on reference material, panel selection and measurement procedures. This will enable workers in this country and Europe to adopt common standards.

Despite the reservations on its subjectivity, olfactometry is able to:

(i)   Provide a direct measure of the environmental effect of the emission;
(ii) Differentiate between those compounds which smell, and others which do not; and,
(iii) Weight the components of the odour according to their threshold of detection.

5.4 Odour-Abatement Techniques

5.4.1 Prevention and control. There is a requirement under the Environmental

MAY 1991

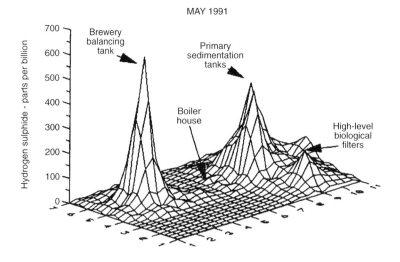

Odour map of Manor Farm STW before remedial work

MAY 1992

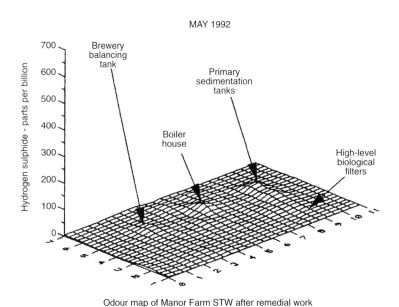

Odour map of Manor Farm STW after remedial work

Fig. 22. Odour maps of Manor Farm before and after remedial work

Protection Act to prevent odour nuisance, and schemes for extension or refurbishment of sewage-treatment works incorporate equipment and procedures to minimize odour nuisance. These are simple precautions and are described as follows:

(i)   Reduce the amount of sludge and the period of time it is held in the primary and secondary settlement tanks by the use of automatic desludging;

(ii) Minimize the storage of raw or unstable sludge;

(iii) Design plant to minimize turbulence and exposure of sludge to the atmosphere, avoiding falls of liquors from pipes and weirs into open tanks;

(iv) Provide equipment to keep the plant clear of scum and grease;

(v)   Avoid recycling odorous liquors (such as supernatant and filtrate) to the inlet works where emissions may occur;

(vi) Prevent the release of odours by covering and ventilating sludge sumps, storage tanks, manholes and other points where release may occur;

(vii) Buildings where odours occur should be maintained at a slightly negative pressure by ventilation fans to minimize leakage to the atmosphere;

(viii) Provide local extraction and treatment at locations of high concentrations of odour such as storage tanks and centrifuges; and

(ix) Within buildings the ventilation system should direct air from areas of low odour to areas of higher risk.

It is implicit in these ordinary measures that odour prevention needs to be considered at the commencement of a scheme; the earlier it is considered, the less it costs, and the greater the assurance of success.

Road-traffic fumes contain some of the same compounds (e.g. hydrogen sulphide) which are likely to be found on sewage-treatment works, but at concentrations likely to be below the threshold of detection. Sometimes minor increases in the environmental concentrations of these compounds can suddenly make an odour apparent. The traffic may be the major contributor, but the sewage works will be considered to be the source, and this is one reason why urban sites need careful planning for odour control.

5.4.2 Dilution and dispersion. Dilution of an odorous gas stream with a large quantity of air can reduce the concentration of the compound to below its threshold level. This may appear to be an attractive and cheap option, but it is not good practice because it does not alter the mass of contaminant discharged, and also because the larger the volume, the less the capacity of the environment to dilute it.

Dispersion alone is not sufficient for large odour sources or high concentrations but, after treatment, some form of dispersion is necessary. Odour-treatment plants are vented through stacks, and the height to obtain acceptable dispersion is considered to be 1.5 times the height of any nearby building. The use of chimneys is legitimate and effective, because it aids the dispersion process and, in particular, protects nearby properties. The choice of whether to use a chimney or treat to a higher standard is essentially an economic one: the higher the volume, the more attractive a chimney will be. Accordingly, there are very few sewage-treatment sites where the discharge of odour through a chimney has been cost effective.

The evaluation of atmospheric dispersion, particularly from point sources such as a chimney, is (in theory) well established[25] using a combination of dispersion models and statistical approaches. This approach, however, needs to be used with care. Most dispersion models are based on those originally developed for water pollution studies, and tend to be time-averaged predictions of concentration. This is relevant for modelling other environmental accumulations, but odours are perceived to be a momentary concentration above a threshold. Generally, the more dilute the odour, the shorter the time period and the nearer the source, the less accurate is the prediction. Some models are now available where the results take the more useful form of a probability function of the concentration exceeding a given value.

5.4.3 Odour-masking agents and counteractants. Masking agents and counteractants have been widely used at sewage-treatment works to spray into the air, often around the perimeter of the works. Some are intended to submerge the smell in a more pleasant one (a masking agent), while others change the way odours are perceived (counteractants). Although serving a useful purpose as short-term palliatives, neither method is a long-term solution for a serious odour problem.

The chemical is forced by compressed air through atomizers suspended from posts about 4 m above the ground, and the spray mist forms a curtain through which smells have to pass. The technique is not always reliable because it depends on achieving the correct balance of agent and odour, and on the wind direction. Wind speed and direction equipment can reduce the amount of chemical used, but the systems tend to be expensive to operate although they are cheap to install. The method is often used for odours from sludge handling plants, particularly where the odours are intermittent and diffuse, or difficult to enclose such as from drying beds and open storage tanks.

5.4.4 Chemical dosing. Chemicals, principally lime, have been used for centuries to counteract odour nuisance. The bacterial activity which forms odorous compounds can be inhibited if sufficient lime or caustic soda is added to increase the pH of the sludge to a very high value. However, although this will inhibit the production of hydrogen sulphide, the alkaline conditions promote the release of ammonia and other alkaline compounds.

Chemicals (notably iron compounds) may be used in digesters to convert sulphides to insoluble forms, and this also reduces the concentration of hydrogen sulphide in the digester gas. However, complex iron phosphates may form and restrict flow in pipework, and the fixation of sulphide with iron salts may be reversed under acidic conditions.

5.5 Odour Treatment

Both chemical and biological treatment systems are used to remove odours and they each have application to particular treatment sites. Toogood[26] summarized advantages and disadvantages of some of the processes available and these are reproduced in Table 19.

5.5.1 Wet scrubbing. Contaminated air, extracted by the ventilation fans, is passed through a tower packed with media to provide a high surface area, and is normally wetted with final effluent. As the odorous gas rises through the wetted media, it dissolves and is oxidized by the reagents added to the system. The design of scrubbing systems has to incorporate storage and handling of chemicals, and the disposal of the effluent has to be carefully considered.

Types of scrubbing systems:

(i)   Towers packed with media with counter-current recirculation of the scrubbing liquor to provide a high gas-liquid contact area;

(ii)   Cross-flow versions of packed towers, enabling several stages to be used in one pass of air; and

(iii)   Spray columns in which the scrubbing liquor is pumped through a fine spray at the top of the column to contact the upward flowing contaminated gas.

Reagents used in scrubbing liquors:

(i)   Water or final effluent is often used as a first step on a 'once through' basis, to remove ammonia and amines;

(ii)   Sulphuric acid or other acids provide more efficient treatment of ammonia and amines;

(iii)   Sodium hydroxide is used to remove acidic compounds such as hydrogen sulphide;

(iv)   Sodium hypochlorite (normally used in conjunction with sodium hydroxide) oxidizes sulphides and most organic-nitrogen compounds. It

Table 19. Odour Treatment Processes

Process	Advantages	Disadvantages
Chemical scrubbing	Standard technology Easy to monitor and control Good performance if multi-stage Quick to re-establish after breakdown Handles rapid variations in odour	High capital and operating costs Storage of hazardous chemicals
Wet ozone scrubbing	Meets high standard if appropriately designed Single stage process No chemical storage	Expensive to build and operate Ozone residual may be an odour May need chemicals for pH correction
Adsorption with carbon and oxidizing packing	Good as a polishing process Cheap to install Removes volatile organic compounds	High operating costs Not good for high sulphides Affected by humidity
Bioscrubbers	Low operating costs Robust Good for high sulphide levels	Cannot achieve high standards Sulphides may inhibit performance with other compounds
Biofilters	Simple to operate Familiar technology Reliable performance	Large plan area Difficult to re-commission Less effective with very high sulphide levels

is less effective for aldehydes and ketones, and some of the lower amines may be converted to chloramines which have their own unpleasant odour. Other oxidants such as chlorine dioxide, potassium permanganate and hydrogen peroxide, are generally less effective, or more expensive than sodium hypochlorite, although they may be appropriate for particular malodorous compounds. Sodium metabisulphite may be used in a later stage to remove chlorine; and

(v)   Ozone has been used effectively, dissolved in the recirculation water, and has advantages of being generated on site and minimizing the build-up of reaction products in the scrubbing liquor.

Multi-stage scrubbing

For complex mixtures of odorous compounds which are often experienced at sludge treatment plants, several stages of scrubbing may be needed (Fig. 23). The first stage is slightly acidic in order to remove lower amines which could form chloramines in the next stage.

Stage 1:   scrubbing in a spray column with water or final effluent on a 'once through' basis;

Stage 2:   scrubbing in a packed column with a sulphuric acid wash to complete removal of ammonia and amines; and

Stage 3:   oxidation of sulphides and organic compounds with sodium hypochlorite under alkaline conditions (pH 9–11).

Where very alkaline conditions are required to remove sulphides using hypochlorite, scrubbing with sodium thiosulphate in a further stage may be necessary to eliminate the smell of chlorine compounds released from the previous column.

There is an increased pressure drop with multiple columns, and intermediate ventilation blowers may be needed, especially if only the gases with the highest contamination receive full treatment, less contaminated air being input part way through the system.

5.5.2 Adsorption columns. Deodorization may be achieved by passing the contaminated air through a bed of adsorbent media impregnated with chemicals to oxidize or inactivate the odorous compounds. Suppliers frequently refer to this as 'dry scrubbing'. Examples of types of adsorbent media include activated carbon and activated alumina.

Activated carbon has been used as a simple and effective treatment for odours and toxic gases since early this century (Fig. 24 and Plates 4 and 5). The raw materials from which the coke or charcoal is produced include coal, peat, wood and coconut shell. It is then heat-treated with steam at 800–1000°C to increase the pore size. There are many types of activated carbon available, but normally the granules are 2 mm or less, and the microporous structure (pores around 2 nanometre diameter) provides a very high specific surface area of 750–1500 m^2/g.

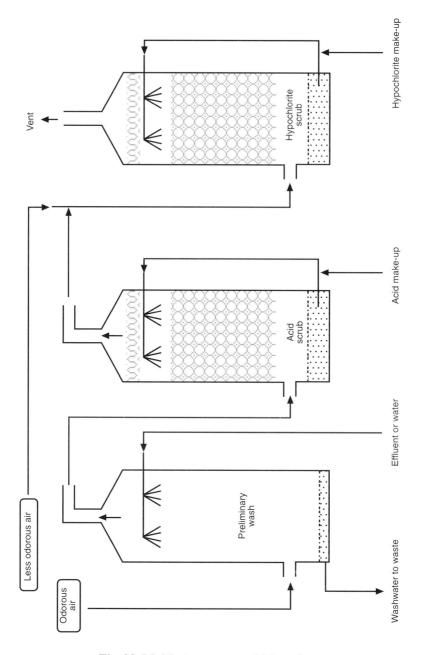

Fig. 23. Multi-stage wet scrubbing plant

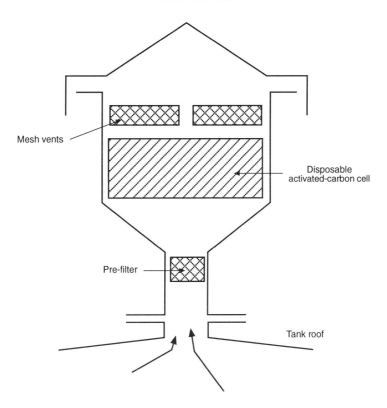

Mesh vents

Disposable
activated-carbon cell

Pre-filter

Tank roof

Fig. 24. Passive activated-carbon unit

Activated alumina may be impregnated with sodium hydroxide for the removal of sulphur and chlorine compounds; potassium permanganate to oxidize hydrogen sulphide, indoles, skatoles and mercaptans; and sodium thiosulphate which is effective for amines, ammonia and other nitrogen compounds.

Odorous air is passed through one or more beds of media, depending on the mixture of compounds present. It is essential to eliminate both mist and condensation moisture to avoid wetting the media, and high-efficiency mist eliminators and insulated ducts are important for sewage-works applications. Sometimes the beds may be heated as an additional measure.

It is important to prevent contamination of the bed with dust particles, as these can seriously interfere with the efficiency of the process and increase the pressure drop through the bed. Over a period of time (usually less than 1 year), the reagents in the media become exhausted and have to be replaced.

Plate 4. Passive activated-carbon unit

These systems have a very low pressure drop and short contact times, but with a relatively high cost of media replacement. They are best used in applications with high volumes of relatively low contamination or, in sensitive locations, as a polishing process.

5.5.3 Biological treatment. Micro-organisms are capable of oxidizing many odorous compounds to simple, non-odorous compounds such as carbon dioxide; and, as with a biological filter at the sewage works, the essential requirements are a high surface area for the growth of biomass, oxygen, and water (final effluent) to carry the odorous material. The odorous compounds and oxygen are dissolved in water and exposed to biomass attached to the media and oxidized by the bacteria. There are two variants, i.e. bioscrubbers and biofilters.

Bioscrubbers and biofilters are used where there are high concentrations of odour. To remove low residual concentrations, a polishing stage (such as dry adsorption column) may be needed.

Bioscrubbers. Final effluent is recirculated around a column of packing media on which the biofilm grows. This keeps the film layer moist and provides trace nutrients, such as phosphorus and metals, which are necessary for the growth of biomass. The odorous gas is blown in from below, and as it passes over the wetted medium the odour-producing compounds are oxidized by the micro-organisms. A proportion of the recirculated liquor is discharged from the system to remove the oxidation products and to allow for replenishment of nutrients. This is controlled by monitoring the pH of the liquor.

Bioscrubbing is used mainly for dealing with high concentrations of hydrogen sulphide, and is able to deal with concentrations of several hundred parts per million, beyond which solubility limits performance. Because bioscrubbers can treat high inlet concentrations and are limited by outlet concentration rather than the percentage removal, they are appropriate to schemes which minimize volume flows.

Plate 5. Fan-assisted activated-carbon unit drawing from sludge press house

Biofilters. Biofilters were developed from earlier work with soil beds in the late

1970s, and are often known as peat beds (Fig. 25 and Plate 6) because this is the most common material used. From an early stage in development it was found to be an advantage to include alternate layers of a structured material such as heather. Heather also supports biological growth, but its main purpose is to provide the structure to prevent short-circuiting which can result from compaction of the peat. Other materials used have always been of natural origin, and include compost, bark, wood chips and spruce twigs. Biofilters are inexpensive to install and operate having only a fan and sprinkling system to maintain.

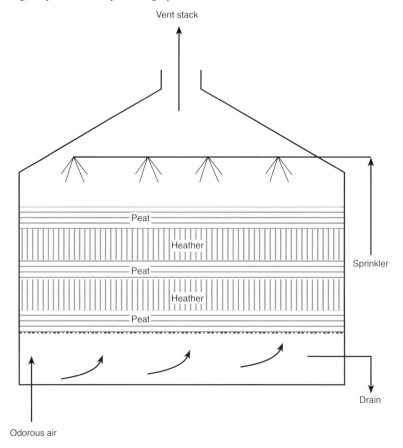

Fig. 25. Peat-bed biofilter

Normally the medium has a life of 3–5 years, depending on the application and loading. Adequate moisture is also of prime importance, especially with peat fibre which cannot be re-wetted once it has dried out. If the concentration of hydrogen sulphide is more that about 15 ppm, surface sprinklers are needed to irrigate the surface to prevent the accumulation of acid which would lead to eventual failure[27]. At concentrations of sulphides greater than this, bioscrubbers are recommended. Biofilters are inexpensive to maintain because they are self-regulating, and the fan is the only moving part.

Plate 6. Peat-based biofilter at Minworth sewage-treatment works

If final effluent is not used as the wetting medium, the addition of bacterial cultures may be beneficial to speed up the often slow process of commissioning (weeks), or to build up a specific population such as specialist sulphur bacteria for sulphide removal. Biofilters which are used to treat non-natural contaminants (such as toluene from paint-spraying booths) require inoculation with biomass prior to commissioning.

5.5.4 Thermal oxidation. The oxidation of odorous compounds by combustion with a fuel has been used in many industries. This process is particularly appropriate where there are high concentrations of odours, and it can handle both wet and dusty gases. It is effective for most classes of odour compound, but the high operating costs cause it to be used for gas streams containing toxic or harmful material. However, with the increasing use of incineration or drying for sludge treatment, the combustion air could include air which is ventilated from odour sources.

Temperatures of over 800°C are necessary for complete odour destruction, and further control on the exhaust gas is required to comply with emission standards.

5.6 Sources of Odour

5.6.1 Tanker reception. Sludge which is collected or delivered by tanker is likely to give rise to some odour. The displacement of the air as tankers fill, or vacuum tankers exhaust, can be controlled by connecting the tanker vent to an odour-control system when circumstances demand.

For a large works with a centralized odour-control facility, this additional gas stream may be diluted with the other sources. For smaller works a simple, robust, system suitable for discontinuous operation, such as dry scrubbing or activated carbon, could be appropriate.

5.6.2 Sludge storage. It is preferable to minimize sludge storage before thickening and processing. Anaerobic conditions can establish within a few days (or hours) under favourable conditions, and the odours released by disturbance of the sludges when filling and emptying. Tanks should normally be covered and frequently need to be ventilated to an odour-control system, either with forced ventilation or to a small passive biofilter.

5.6.3 Sludge thickening. Continuous gravity thickeners release less odour than batch units because the liquid level does not fluctuate. Thickeners need to be covered, but at less sensitive sites odour treatment may not be necessary. Continuous picket-fence thickeners can be regarded as part of the general odour-control strategy, because they minimize the sludge age and reduce the amount of sludge which is held.

5.6.4 Sludge digestion. Digested sludge has much less odour during subsequent storage, treatment and disposal because most of the volatile organic solids have been converted to methane and carbon dioxide. The potential for odour normally diminishes by about 90%$^{(28)}$, and that remaining is largely associated with trapped bubbles of digester gas, and therefore odour control is concentrated on the digester gas. Surplus gas is flared-off in a stack. The sulphide content of the gas is dependent on the presence of sulphate in the sewage, either from the water supply or from saline intrusion.

When the gas is used in a combined heat and power (CHP) system it may require treatment to reduce the concentration of sulphide to less than 500 ppm. However, in practice it has been found more economical to use a chemical additive and to change the engine oil frequently.

Air is sometimes blown through digested sludge to strip residual gases and to promote cooling and consolidation, as described on page 49. The vented air can be very odorous and may require treatment.

5.6.5 Sludge dewatering. In the process of dewatering, sludge my be subjected to considerable turbulence and contact with the atmosphere. Mechanical dewatering plant is normally housed within a building, therefore adequate ventilation and odour control has to be provided to ensure a safe working environment. Since the industry moved from lime conditioning to the use of polyelectrolytes, odour release has changed from ammoniacal odours to acidic odours such as sulphides and fatty acids. This has led to increased potential for odour nuisance because sulphides have a very much lower threshold of detection than ammonia.

The air stream from a centrifuge is fairly readily segregated, the equipment being effectively enclosed, and may be extracted to discharge to an odour-control system which is suitable for high concentrations of odour. For filter belt presses, often open to the atmosphere, ventilation hoods are used to contain and extract the odours.

In selecting dewatering equipment to minimize odours, examination of the provision for filtrate or centrate handling is important. The filtrate is more odorous than cake, and open drainage systems should be avoided.

5.6.6 Sludge drying. The drying of sludges involves intensive contact with hot air, and most odorous compounds are volatilized into the air stream. Condensation of the vapour produces a hot liquor with potential for odour nuisance, and it therefore must be handled with the minimum of turbulence and not exposed to the atmosphere.

Non-condensed vapours are very odorous and may be fed (as part of the combustion air) to the drier burner. Scrubbing of the burner exhaust gases may be required before dispersion through a stack.

Dried sludge often has a residual odour, and care is required in handling and storage to control odour release and dust. The drier building should be ventilated, with consideration given to odour control of the vented air.

5.6.7 Sludge incineration. Sludge incineration processes subject the sludge, together with any odorous compounds, to temperatures in excess of $800°C$ which should ensure complete destruction. Effective and stringent exhaust gas control is now required to minimize the release to the atmosphere of other materials such as dust, heavy metals and oxides of sulphur and nitrogen. The combustion process can often be used for odour treatment.

6. Sludge Strategy Concepts

6.1 Introduction

Until the late 1970s and early 1980s, sludge disposal from a particular sewage-treatment works was usually decided on the basis of (i) the lowest cost option (subject to its legality), (ii) its convenience, and (iii) its operational security over a reasonable period of time. The impact of the disposal operation on the environment and the long-term sustainability of the option were not usually given much, if any, consideration. However, during recent years, and particularly since the mid-1980s, there has been a recognition that the overall route for treatment and disposal of sludge from a sewage-treatment works, or a groups of works, should be selected primarily to minimize any adverse impacts on the environment. Subject to that requirement being satisfied, and if several options present themselves, the final choice of route or routes should be made on the basis of (a) minimizing costs, (b) practicality, and (c) the achievement of long-term operational security.

This approach is the essential basis of the 'best practicable environmental option' (BPEO) study which now forms an essential primary component of the strategic planning of sludge disposal in the UK. The BPEO study has been of particular importance since 1990 in identifying the most appropriate land-based options to replace the sea routes.

The UK management of sewage-treatment and sludge-disposal facilities is based upon large geographical and/or political boundaries. This enables sewage-treatment works to be grouped together to suit the management needs of the organization. The treatment and disposal of sludge can be considered in the light of these regional groupings, and solutions can be developed to meet both the local and regional needs. Both short-term and long-term solutions can be considered in the light of a sustainable strategic plan.

The environment is high on the political agenda: public awareness to all environmental issues is increasing, and local communities take an interest in sewage treatment and disposal. In the UK there has been an attempt to keep ahead of public opinion through research and publication of guidelines. However, as an additional safeguard, local councils can now request 'environmental impact assessments' as part of the planning process.

Sludge treatment and disposal is a major cost in the overall objective of treating wastewater. Calcutt and Moss[29] showed that 50% of the operating costs of a sewage-treatment plant were associated with sludge treatment and disposal but, at that time, only 15% of the capital investment was in sludge facilities.

The UK is predicting an increase in sludge production of about 60% by 1999 and a virtual doubling of the sludge production (to 2.1 million tDS/annum) by the year 2006.

An important change to take place in the UK is the cessation of sea disposal at the end of 1998. The UK will then need to provide a total land-based solution for sludge disposal. With 20% of the sludge expected to be disposed of by incineration, land recycling must be expanded. It is anticipated that agricultural land will provide the main option, and that disposal to this outlet will double by the year 2006.

6.2 Strategy Concept

The necessity of having a strategic plan to dispose of sludge in the face of legislative and economic constraints is fundamental to the survival of any business whose success depends upon the safe disposal of the waste which it produces. This implies that a long-term view has to be taken if the business is to stay trading beyond the life of today's management.

The strategy is a management tool which embraces the objectives of a company, and provides a framework for sensible investment and operational practice. It is not cast in 'tablets of stone', but has to be responsive to change without severe distortion of its original concepts. If properly conceived, it will protect the company from increasing operating constraints and will maximize benefits to the company.

The key to any successful strategy is an understanding of the problem. This is not just a question of collecting sludge production and disposal data and processing it through a computer. It starts with a basic understanding as to how and why sludge is produced, followed by an assessment of its potential to harm or improve the business by way of threats or opportunities. It goes on to provide a long-term, sustainable solution.

One technique is to use the 'greenfield' concept. This represents the ideal environmental solution, independent of the constraints surrounding the current assets. It is a base line against which judgement can be made about the value of existing assets towards meeting the strategic objectives.

The development of the strategy takes account of:

(i)   Current legislative demands;
(ii)   Likely future legislative trends;
(iii)   The company's business objectives;
(iv)   The influences of external regulators;
(v)   The technology which is currently available;
(vi)   The potential for advances and the introduction of new technology;
(vii)   The time-related viability of existing disposal outlets;
(viii)   The potential to develop new outlets; and
(ix)   Economic and cost implications.

6.3 Team Approach

The development of a successful strategy requires the combination of technical, operational, legal, planning, economic and financial skills. Success is dependent on a thinking process extending beyond today's problems into the prediction of future events and the risks associated with them.

It is essential that the development of the strategic plan is led by an integrated team which is aware of the following needs:

(i)   It should be led by a senior manager with vision, and committed to the ownership of the strategy and its implementation;
(ii)   The team should be of mixed disciplines to formulate the strategy;
(iii)   There must be a clear brief including time constraints;
(iv)   Regular meetings should take place between the executive management and team leader; and
(v)   The team must sell the strategy throughout the organization, and thereby secure extended ownership.

6.4 Strategy Development

For a large geographic area dealing with a large range of sewage-treatment and water-treatment plants, it is unlikely that there will be a single common solution. Usually the strategy will have a mixed solution enabling the small works to be served by treatment centres, either by concentrating treatment facilities at a larger works or at a treatment centre. The strategy will also provide flexibility in the event of failure of one particular route for a short period, and some strategies include strategic storage in case of such events.

A good strategy will (a) ensure long-term security, (b) maintain maximum flexibility, (c) secure the sewage-treatment works against failure to comply with quality standards, (d) enable sensible investment, (e) promote a sound company image in a 'green environment', (f) provide a framework for research and development programmes, and (g) keep the company in business.

The key stages in developing a strategy can be described as follows:

(i)   *Define the mission statement.* For example, dispose of all the sludge produced by the organization over the next 25 years, within the prevailing legal framework, without causing a public-health risk, nuisance or harm to the environment, and to achieve this at minimum cost. Wherever possible, beneficial recycling will be promoted including product enhancement to improve return of investment through sales;

(ii)   *Identify the legal and environmental constraints.* This should include present constraints and a prediction of likely changes such as a review of the EC sludge to land Directive[(30)], and more restriction on metals and organics released to environment;

(iii) *Define the company's environmental policy with respect to sludge.* This may include the mission statement but would be more comprehensive and capable of withstanding public scrutiny;

(iv)   *Collect data.* This would include present and future sludge production and current outlets, and take account of quality as well as quantity;

(v)   *Identify new outlets and determine their capacity.* A series of 'what if?' scenarios should be prepared to simulate possible future constraints, and match production to outlet availability for any one year. This may require the use of a predictive model to evaluate the options, especially for a wide geographical area and a large number of outlets;

(vi)   *Review the treatment options.* It is important to consider emerging technologies, and there could be a need to change other policies such as control over industrial effluent;

(vii) *Consider the capital and operating cost implications.* When the overall least-cost solution has been found, consider the implications on existing assets;

(viii) *Refine the detailed strategy to maximize existing investment, avoiding future capital redundancy;*

(ix)   *Profile the investment needs;* and

(x)   *Adopt the strategy and commence the implementation.*

6.5 Role of Process Technology

The role of process technology is to provide a cost-effective means of making the sludge suitable for the chosen outlet. A strategy should first identify the outlets and constraints and develop a process flow sheet, matching the product to the outlet requirements. A mixed management system will usually be developed, for example to incinerate a minimum quantity of sludge in order to provide a sustainable liquid recycling route for the remainder.

Process technology may be used to improve the product acceptability and, in some cases, add value to the product. Examples of this may be a plan to replace the liquid outlet with dried granules or pellets which the farmer may find more acceptable and for which he may be prepared to pay a higher price.

6.6 European Policy and UK Legislation

The legislative framework within which sludge utilization and disposal has to be practised has become much more complicated and restrictive since 1974 when the Control of Pollution Act Part II was introduced. In effect, virtually every activity associated with sludge utilization and disposal is subject to some regulation, and the regulatory requirements have to be taken into account in the planning, consultation and implementation stages of every sludge disposal operation. As a convenient reference, Table 20 provides a summary of the main legislative controls relevant to sludge utilization and disposal activities. The information applies specifically to England and Wales, and the requirements in Scotland and Northern Ireland are generally similar.

6.6.1 EC sludge to land Directive. The Directive[30] encourages recycling of sludge to agriculture. It was implemented by member states in 1989 through national legislation, which is often more stringent than the Directive itself, to protect the local soils.

The Directive has the dual purpose of (a) ensuring safeguards against harmful effects of spreading sewage sludge, and (b) promoting the correct use of the sludge on agricultural land.

Sewage sludge must not be spread on agricultural land where the concentration of certain metals in the soil exceeds levels laid down in regulations by the Government. Sludge must be treated before use, but the Government may authorize the use of untreated sludge if it is injected or worked into the soil. Comprehensive records are to be kept and made available to competent authorities on request.

Table 20. Summary of legislative framework relevant to sludge disposal

	Definition of activity relating to use or disposal of sludge	Main examples in practice	Designated a 'controlled waste'?	Requires registration with Waste Regulation Authority?	Waste management licence required?	Principal regulating legislation
1	Treating, keeping or disposal within curtilage of sewage works as an integral part of works' operation	Final disposal within curtilage of works from which sludge originated	No	Yes	No	B
2	Supplying or using in accordance with Sludge (Use in Agriculture) Regulations	Utilization of sludge on arable land, grassland, orchards nurseries, horticulture etc.	No	No	No	A
3	As above	Use on 'dedicated land'	No	No	No	A
4	Spreading on land which is not agricultural land if it results in ecological improvement	Use in forests, woods and some other beneficial uses	Yes	Yes	No	A, B
5	Spreading on any land in connection with reclamation or improvement of that land	Use in land-reclamation schemes	Yes	Yes	No	A, B
6	Spreading on non-agricultural land without ecological improvement	Deposition on tips and at landfill sites	Yes	Yes	Yes	B
7	Storage in a secure container or lagoon of sludge intended to be used in accordance with Activity 2 above	Storage of sludge on agricultural land on which sludge is intended to be spread	No	No	No	B
8	Storage at the place where it is intended to be spread of sludge intended for use in accordance with activities 4 or 5 above	Storage of sludge at a reclamation site or forestry site for intended use on that site	Yes	Yes	No	B
9		Disposal at sea by vessel	No	No	No	C
10		Disposal to sea via pipeline	No	No	No	C

(A) Sludge (Use in Agriculture) Regulations 1989

(B) Environmental Protection Act 1990, Controlled Waste Regulations 1992, Waste Management Licensing Regulations 1994

(C) Food and Environmental Protection Act 1985

6.6.2 Deposition of sludge on land. The primary legislation affecting the use of all land-based outlets for sludge are (a) the Environmental Protection Act 1990 Part II[31], (b) the relevant regulations made under that Act[32,33], and (c) the regulations concerning the use of sludge in agriculture[2] made under the European Communities Act. In principle, the legislation is designed to encourage the beneficial recycling of sludge whilst strictly regulating the way it is used in order to avoid environmental damage.

6.6.3 Disposal of sludge to sea. The disposal of sludge to sea from a ship is regulated by the Food and Environmental Protection Act 1974[34], and is subject to government licence. The relatively rare use of pipelines to discharge sludge to the marine environment is covered by the Water Resources Act 1991. All forms of disposal of sludge to sea will be banned after 1998 under the urban wastewater treatment Directive[35].

6.6.4 Sewage sludge as a 'controlled waste'. A very important feature of the regulations defining 'controlled wastes' and the waste management licensing regulations for such wastes, is that sewage sludge (or septic tank sludge) is designated a 'controlled industrial waste' except when it is supplied or used in accordance with the Sludge (Use in Agriculture) Regulations[2] when it is not then a 'controlled waste'.

This vital distinction means that sludges used in agriculture (or even on non-agricultural land), in accordance with the Sludge (Use in Agriculture) Regulations[2], are not subject to the Waste Management Licensing Regulations.

6.6.5 Urban wastewater treatment Directive. The Directive[35] stipulates minimum levels of treatment to be achieved by certain dates between 1998 and 2005, depending on the size of works. The articles of specific interest are:

Article 14 (1)
Sludge arising from wastewater treatment shall be re-used whenever appropriate. Disposal routes shall minimize the adverse effects on the environment.

Article 14 (2)
Competent authorities or appropriate bodies shall ensure that before 31 December 1998 the disposal of sludge from urban wastewater treatment plants is subject to general rules or registration or authorization.

Article 14 (3)
Member states shall ensure that, before 31 December 1998, the disposal of sludge to surface waters by dumping from ships, by discharge from pipelines, or other

means, is phased out.

Article 14 (4)
Until the elimination of disposal mentioned in para (3), member states shall ensure that the total amount of toxic, persistent or bioaccumulable materials in sludge disposed of to surface waters is licensed for disposal and progressively reduced.

6.6.6 Duty of care. An important feature of the Environmental Protection Act 1990 is the principle of 'duty of care' with respect to controlled wastes. This principle (which is legally binding) is that any person who produces, conveys, keeps, treats, or disposes of a controlled waste, or otherwise has control of such wastes, is bound to take all reasonable measures to ensure that (a) no person contravenes the law regarding the disposal of the waste, (b) the escape of the waste from his control or that of another person is prevented, and (c) if the waste is transferred to another person it is only to an authorized person, and that the authorized person receives sufficient written description of the waste to enable him to avoid contravening the law regarding its disposal.

It is important to note that the 'duty of care' principle does not apply to sludge used in accordance with the Sludge (Use in Agriculture) Regulations[2] since the sludge then is not a controlled waste. However, the latter regulations themselves include essentially the same provisions as the 'duty of care' regulations.

6.6.7 Other directives, laws and regulations. There is now a complex mixture of changing international conventions, EC directives and national legislation relevant to the treatment and disposal of sludge. A strategy evaluation must consider the legislation which is likely at the time of implementing the strategy. In the UK, there is no single piece of legislation which covers sewage sludge, and it is imperative that the search encompasses all legislation.

6.7 UK Application

6.7.1 British code of practice. The use of sewage sludge in agriculture Directive[30] was enforced in the UK under the Sludge (Use in Agriculture) Regulations 1989. To accompany these regulations the DoE published a Code of Practice[36]. One of the main features of this Code is a classification of effective treatment processes which will satisfy the Code's requirements (Table 21).

6.7.2 Other legislation. Other national legislation is derived from the Environmental

Table 21. Effective Treatment Processes under UK Regulations

Process	Description
Sludge pasteurization	Minimum of 30 min at 70°C or minimum of 4 h at 55°C (or appropriate intermediate conditions), followed in all cases by primary mesophilic anaerobic digestion
Mesophilic anaerobic digestion	Mean retention period of at least 12 days primary digestion in temperature range 35°C $\pm 3^\circ$C or at least 20 days primary digestion in temperature range 25°C $\pm 3^\circ$C followed (in each case) by a secondary stage which provides a mean retention period of at least 14 days
Thermophilic anaerobic digestion	Mean retention period of at least 7 days digestion. All sludge to be subject to a minimum of 55°C for a period of 4 h
Composting(windrows or aerated piles)	The compost must be maintained at 40°C for at least 5 days and for 4 h during this period at a minimum of 55°C within the body of the pile, followed by a period of maturation adequate to ensure that the compost reduction process is substantially complete
Lime stabilization of liquid sludge	Addition of lime to raise the pH to 12.0 and sufficient to ensure that the pH is not less than 12 for a minimum period of 2 h. The sludge can be used directly
Liquid storage	Storage of untreated liquid sludge for a minimum period of 3 months
Dewatering and storage	Conditioning of untreated sludge with lime or other coagulants followed by dewatering and storage of the cake for a minimum period of 3 months. If the sludge has been subjected to primary mesophilic anaerobic digestion, storage to be for a minimum period 14 days

Protection Act 1990. Integrated Pollution Control (IPC)[37] is a system of pollution control, set up under the Act, intended to apply to the most polluting or technologically complex industrial and other processes throughout England and Wales. The enforcing authority is Her Majesty's Inspectorate of Pollution (HMIP).

The main objectives of IPC are (a) to prevent or minimize the release of prescribed substances, and to render harmless any such substances which are released, and (b) to develop an approach to pollution control which considers discharges from industrial processes to all media in the context of the effect on the environment as a whole.

Other Codes of Practice have been developed to control the disposal of sludge to forestry[38], land restoration[39] and for the protection of water[40].

6.8 BPEO and BATNEEC

6.8.1 Concepts of BPEO and BATNEEC. The concept of 'best practicable environmental option' (BPEO) was first introduced by the Royal Commission on Environmental Pollution in a series of reports of which the twelfth report[41] is devoted exclusively to the BPEO concept and implementation. The Environmental Protection Act 1990 defines 'practicable' as meaning 'reasonably practicable', having regard to local conditions and circumstances, the current state of technical knowledge, and the financial implications.

Under s.7 of the Environmental Protection Act 1990, HMIP have a duty to ensure that the 'best available techniques not entailing excessive cost' (BATNEEC) are used to prevent or minimize the release of prescribed substances.

It is important to draw the distinction between the BATNEEC terminology and the BPEO concept. In short, BATNEEC refers to releases into a named medium and is plant-specific, but BPEO refers to releases into more than one medium. The terms have been incorporated into the Environmental Protection Act 1990.

The term BPEO refers to the quality of the environment as a whole. It is concerned with the overall environmental impact, and takes account of the impact on all the 'mediums' into which there is a release of pollution, and the interactions between them as a result of the release. BPEO therefore involves the making of 'value judgements' which may not necessarily be readily quantifiable. The BPEO study is a rigorous and demanding procedure aimed at satisfying a number of constraints. Since the arguments have to be sustainable, it requires detailed documentation and the establishment of an audit trail which can substantiate the decisions which are taken. Many of the features of a BPEO study would be required to substantiate the decisions put forward in a subsequent 'environmental impact statement'.

6.8.2 BPEO methodology as applied to sewage sludge. Before embarking on the application of BPEO specifically for sludge, HMIP commissioned the Water Research Centre to undertake a study[(42)] to identify the procedure to be followed. This identified the following nine points which must feature in the methodology:

(i)   Long-term effect should be considered in addition to those which would be evident in the short term;

(ii)   Long-range effects as well as those which would be apparent at the short range;

(iii)   An imaginative search for potential options must be made which seeks to change the *status quo*. The scope of this search is to extend from an examination of opportunities to control the quantity and quality of inputs to a sewerage system or systems, to the use of novel outlets;

(iv)   Local factors of a social and political nature are excluded from the considerations. Where a decision to implement an option is taken on these grounds and overrides environmental considerations, this fact must be openly and clearly acknowledged;

(v)   A reasonable balance between benefits and costs should be struck and, whilst a BPEO may not be the cheapest option, the financial implications of adopting the identified BPEO should not be disproportionate;

(vi)   The financial implications should cover both capital and revenue expenditure and, where appropriate, the costs borne by the dischargers to a sewerage system, the water undertaking having operational responsibility, or the public sector;

(vii)   In appropriate circumstances, where their inclusion would help to allay public concern, precautionary measures would be included in the BPEO provided that their cost was not disproportionate;

(viii) The procedure should take into consideration the current state of knowledge concerning the technology available and the potential impact of sludge disposal routes on, for example, human health, flora and fauna, buildings and other environmental targets; and

(ix)   Plans to monitor potential environmental effects should be developed and subsequently implemented, the results reviewed, and any action arising from the review should be taken at the appropriate stage.

Although the above does consider cost, the BPEO philosophy places selection first and foremost on the environmental aspects of alternative practicable options, and the economic factors must take second place.

6.8.3 Recommended procedure. There are nine steps to the recommended procedure and these are given in Table 22.

Table 22. Recommended Procedure

Step	Step description	Comment
1	Objectives and constraints	Identify what is to be achieved by the study and the constraints
2	Collect data on disposal operation	Provides background information on current operation. Quantify the constraints
3	Generate treatment and disposal options	Generate a number of treatment and disposal options for works in the study area
4	Screen treatment and disposal options	Sift the options generated in step 3 to identify options for further evaluation
5	Evaluate treatment and disposal options	Consider environmental impact economic aspects, and operational security
6	Identify preferred option	Select BPEO
7	Review the preferred option	If necessary review the BPEO in more detail to establish its feasibility
8	Presentation of evaluation	Prepare a report on the data-collection methods, generation of options and evaluation procedures
9	Implement and monitor option	Implement BPEO and monitor environmental and economic impact

Throughout the procedure it is necessary to maintain an audit trail. The best way of achieving this is to prepare a quality plan which, in itself, will demand a referencing of the documentation, its flow during the study, and final filing. Where quality action plans are not normally formalized as part of the working instructions, the following key points are recommended[42]:

(i) All sources of primary data and information should be referenced;

(ii) All assumptions should be documented;

(iii) The names and positions of individuals who have made assumptions and judgements should be recorded;

(iv) The methods by which primary and assumed data are used to generate further (secondary) information should be documented;

(v) The justification for any criteria adopted, in order to compare environmental impacts and determine acceptable risks, should be recorded;

(vi)   The flow of information and decision making should be illustrated diagrammatically with a flow chart; and

(vii)   The documentation should be cross-referenced to match the information in the flow chart.

6.9 Strategic Modelling Techniques

The issues involved in a large strategic study can be complex and, in many cases, there may be several possible solutions which could provide an effective solution. The larger regional strategies have to take account of several hundred sewage-treatment plants and several disposal options, and the solutions provided for one treatment centre may have a significant effect on its neighbour. Choices therefore have to be made about the most appropriate solution which will be the most cost effective for a group of works, rather than for a single one.

The complex process of evaluating options can be resolved on a judgemental basis, in accordance with a set of rules built into a decision tree. Using the latter it is possible to evaluate many options using the iteration techniques associated with computer modelling. There are many inter-active variables, and various computer models have been developed which allow the strategist to test the hypothesis and cost the options.

The first model was originally developed by the Water Research Centre in conjunction with Yorkshire Water to evaluate the options for the West Yorkshire Sludge Strategy. WRc then developed the system further to make it available to the water industry on a commercial basis as the 'water industry sludge disposal optimization model' (WISDOM)[43]. Subsequently, other models have been developed to suit particular requirements and, in addition to WISDOM, there are STRATUM[44] (South West Water), DISPEL[45] (Acer), and BOSS (Southern Water).

The models simulate the treatment and disposal of sludge from sewage-treatment works in defined geographical areas, and are used to evaluate a series of selected sludge treatment and disposal options for an area. They make use of 'geographical information systems' to examine the options of land recycling, and can be tailored to an organization's geographical area, and also to its existing policy and disposal requirements.

Models require information such as sludge production, nature and quantity, soil analyses, treatment processes, and disposal outlets. They can carry out evaluations in annual steps over a given period, and 'What if?' scenarios presented. Several treatment processes may be chosen such as consolidation, anaerobic digestion, post-digestion thickening, mechanical dewatering, composting, thermal drying, and incineration. Sludge can be transported between works for treatment, landfill, land reclamation, dedicated land or agriculture. Sludge may be disposed of to agriculture either directly or via a farm lagoon.

The capital and operating costs of any new plant installed during the simulation are calculated by the model, and for each year of the simulation an annual report can be produced detailing the quantity and cost of the sludge treated and disposed of from each works.

Appendix 1

Basis for estimating total raw sludge production in the UK, and quantity for utilization or disposal after anaerobic digestion

Region	Population connected to sewer (1) ($\times 10^6$)	Percentage population served by sewage works providing: (1)				Estimated population served by sewage works providing: (2)				Estimated raw sludge production from sewage works providing: (3)			
		Prelim'y or none	Primary treatment	Second'y treatment	Tertiary treatment	Prelim'y or none	Primary treatment	Second'y treatment	Tertiary treatment	Primary treatment	Second'y treatment	Tertiary treatment	Total
		%				000s				tDS/annum			
Thames	11 529	2	0	85	13	230	0	9 799	1 499	0	279 271	47 462	322 742
Severn Trent	8 226	0	0	68	32	0	0	5 594	2 632	0	159 429	72 570	235 757
North West	6 753	8	22	67	3	540	1 486	4 525	203	28 234	128 962	5 861	163 083
Anglian	5 184	15	8	52	25	778	415	2 696	1 296	7 885	76 836	31 948	122 305
Scotland	4 844	28	26	45	1	1 356	1 259	2 178	48	23 921	62 073	1 427	87 386
Yorkshire	4 684	9	0	87	4	422	0	4 075	187	0	116 375	19 988	121 798
Southern	4 118	33	12	50	5	1 359	494	2 059	206	9 386	58 681	21 760	74 071
Dŵr Cymru	2 922	45	5	48	2	1 315	146	1 403	58	2 774	39 985	1 718	44 441
Northumbrian	2 554	33	38	27	2	843	970	689	51	18 430	19 636	3 754	39 545
Wessex	2 342	10	26	51	13	234	609	1 194	304	11 571	34 029	8 916	54 416
South West	1 358	35	14	33	18	475	190	448	244	3 610	12 768	0	23 454
N Ireland	1 285	20+	20+	50+	10+	257	257	643	129	4 885	18 325	1 696	25 066
Total	55 799					7 809	5 826	35 303	6 857	110 696	1 006 370	217 102	1 314 064

Notes:
(1) Data from 'Water Facts '94'
(2) Calculated from (1)
(3) Calculated from (2) on the assumption that:
    (a) Preliminary (or none) treatment produces no sludge
    (b) Primary treatment produces 19 kg DS/head per annum
    (c) Primary + secondary* treatment produces 28.5 kg DS/head per annum
    (d) Primary + secondary* + tertiary treatment produces 29 kg DS/head per annum

   * Secondary treatment in the UK assumed to be 50% activated sludge treatment and 50% biological filtration on an overall basis.

   + Percentages not given in 'Water Facts '94', and are estimates from various sources.

Estimated production of raw sludge

From the table, total raw sludge production in the UK (1993–94) is estimated at 1.314 million tonnes DS/annum.

Estimated UK sludge production after solids loss by anaerobic digestion

The proportion of raw sludge which is digested varies from region to region and detailed statistics are not available. Overall, about 50% of UK sludge is digested and, using this overall percentage, the quantity of sludge produced for disposal or utilization may be estimated by assuming that raw sludge contains 75% volatile solids and that an average of 45% of volatile solids are destroyed during digestion.

Then, the mass of sludge solids remaining after digestion is:

$$(1.314 \times 0.5 \times 0.75 \times 0.55) + (1.314 \times 0.5 \times 0.25) + (1.314 \times 0.5)$$
$$= 1.09 \text{ m tonnes DS/annum.}$$

REFERENCES

1. THE INSTITUTION OF WATER AND ENVIRONMENTAL MANAGEMENT. Handbooks of UK Wastewater Practice. *Glossary.* 1993.
2. THE SLUDGE (USE IN AGRICULTURE) REGULATIONS 1989. Statutory Instrument No. 1263. As amended by The Sludge (Use in Agriculture) Regulations 1990, Statutory Instrument No. 880. HMSO, London.
3. COLLINGE, V. K. AND BRUCE, A. M. *Sewage Sludge Disposal: A Strategic Review and Assessment of Research Needs.* WRc Technical Report TR166. Water Research Centre, Medmenham, 1981.
4. DEPARTMENT OF THE ENVIRONMENT. *UK Sewage Sludge Survey. Final Report.* Consultants in Environmental Sciences. 1993.
5. BRUCE, A. M. AND BOON, A. G. Aspects of high-rate biological treatment of domestic and industrial waste waters. *Wat. Pollut. Control,* 1971, **70,** (5), 487.
6. HALL, J. E. The need for innovation in sludge treatment and disposal. In: *Innovative Technologies for Sludge Utilization and Disposal.* IWEM Symposium, Chester, December 1994.
7. WATER SERVICES ASSOCIATION. Sewerage, sewage and sludge disposal, Table 4.5. In: *Water Facts 1994.* (Donna Burnell Ed.) Water Services Association, London, 1994.
8. DEE, A., DAY, M. AND CHAMBERS, B. Guidelines for the design and operation of sewage sludge consolidation tanks. *Water Research Centre.* Swindon, UK. April 1994.
9. HOYLAND, G., DEE, A. AND DAY, M. Optimum design of sewage sludge consolidation tanks. *J. Instn. Wat. & Envir. Mangt.,* 1986, **3,** (5), 505–514.
10. HOYLAND, G. AND DAY, M. An evaluation of picket fences for assisting the consolidation of sewage sludges. *Wat. Pollut. Control,* 1986, **85,** (3), 291–303.
11. WARDEN, J. H. The design of rakes for continuous thickeners. *Filtration and Separation,* 1981, **18,** (2), 113–116.
12. BROWN, B. R., WOOD, L. B., AND FINCH, H. J. Experiments on the dewatering of digested and activated sludge. *Wat. Pollut. Control,* 1972, **71,** (1), 61–84.
13. HURLEY, B. J. E., RACHWAL, A. J. AND HATTON, C. J. Consolidation of digested sludge. In: *Sewage Sludge Stabilization and Disinfection.* (A. Bruce, Ed.) Ellis Horwood, Chichester, 1984, 239–255.
14. LYNCH, M. AND STEPHENSON, T. Experiences of digested sludge thickening by Aercon. *J. Instn. Wat. & Envir. Mangt.,* 1994, **8,** (6), 585–591.
15. BURFITT, M. L. The performance of a full-scale sludge flotation plant. *Wat. Pollut. Control,* 1975, **74,** (4), 474–476.
16. ACKERS, P. AND ALLEN, M. C. The laminar flow of sewage sludge through pipelines. *Instn. Publ. Hlth. Eng. J.,* 1980, **8,** 99–106.
17. COLEBROOK, C. F. Turbulent flow in pipes with particular reference to the transition region between the smooth and rough pipe. *J. Instn. Civ. Engrs.,*

1939, **11,** 133.

18. HOBSON, J. A. AND TOOGOOD, S. J. *Odour Nuisance in Waste Water Treatment – Causes and Control.* WRc Report UM 1025, September 1989.

19. THE INSTITUTION OF WATER AND ENVIRONMENTAL MANAGEMENT. Handbooks of UK Wastewater Practice. *Preliminary Processes.* 1992.

20. BOON, A. G. Septicity in sewers: causes, consequences and containment. *J. Instn. Wat. & Envir. Mangt.,* 1992, **6,** (2), 79–90.

21. WARREN SPRING LABORATORY. *Odour Control - A Concise Guide.* (Valentin, H. H. and North, A, A., Eds.) 1980.

22. NEOTRONICS SCIENTIFIC LTD. Neotronics Olfactory Sensing Equipment (NOSE). Publication 058-0203-00, 1994.

23. SCHOLES, P. Odour control in practice: an end to odour at two well-known sites. In: *Odour Control and Prevention in the Water Industry.* IWEM Symposium, Newcastle University, April 1994.

24. BRENNAN, B. M. AND KENNY, N. Recent advances in odour treatment. In: *Odour Control and Prevention in the Water Industry.* IWEM Symposium, Newcastle University, April 1994.

25. NORTH, A. A. *Odours at Sewage Treatment Works.* WRc Report TR126, December 1979.

26. TOOGOOD, S. Odour control at coastal sites - planning for successful schemes. In: *Odour Control and Prevention in the Water Industry.* IWEM Symposium, Newcastle University, April 1994.

27. BOLTON, E., BRENNAN, B. AND DONLON, M. Peat bio-filtration as an odour control technology, In: *Odour Control and Prevention in the Water Industry.* IWEM Symposium, Newcastle University, April 1994.

28. TOOGOOD, S. J. AND DIAPER, J. Developments in the assessment of odours from sludges. In: *Odour Prevention and Control of Organic Sludge and Livestock Farming.* (Nielsen, V. C., Voorburg, J. H. and l'Hermite, P. Eds.) Elsevier Applied Science Publishers, 1986.

29. CALCUTT, T. AND MOSS, J. Sewage treatment and disposal – the way ahead. *Wat. Pollut. Control,* 1984, **83,** (2), 163–171.

30. COUNCIL OF EUROPEAN COMMUNITIES. Directive on the protection of the environment, and in particular of the soil, when sewage sludge is used in agriculture (86/278/EEC). *Official Journal* L181. 4 July 1986.

31. ENVIRONMENTAL PROTECTION ACT, 1990. HMSO, London, 1990.

32. WASTE MANAGEMENT LICENSING REGULATIONS 1994. *Statutory Instrument No. 1056.* HMSO, London, 1994.

33. CONTROLLED WASTE REGULATIONS 1992. *Statutory Instrument No. 588.* HMSO, London, 1992.

34. FOOD AND ENVIRONMENT PROTECTION ACT 1985. Chapter 48. HMSO, London, 1985.

35. COUNCIL OF EUROPEAN COMMUNITIES. Directive concerning urban waste water

treatment (91/271/EEC). *Official Journal* L135/40. 21 May 1991.

36. DEPARTMENT OF THE ENVIRONMENT. *Code of Practice for Agricultural Use of Sewage Sludge.* HMSO, 1989 & 1992.

37. DEPARTMENT OF THE ENVIRONMENT AND THE WELSH OFFICE. *Integrated Pollution Control – A Practical Guide.* HMIP, London. 1991.

38. WATER RESEARCH CENTRE. *A Manual of Good Practice for the Use of Sewage Sludge in Forestry.* WRc and Forestry Commission, Bulletin 107, HMSO 1992.

39. HALL, J. E. The Use of Sewage Sludge in Land Restoration. Draft Code of Practice, WRc Report PRS 1783-M/2, 1989.

40. MINISTRY OF AGRICULTURE. *A Code of Good Agricultural Practice for the Protection of Water.* PB 0587, July 1991.

41. ROYAL COMMISSION ON ENVIRONMENTAL POLLUTION. *Twelth Report.* Best Practicable Environmental Option. Cmnd. 310. HMSO, London, 1988.

42. WATER RESEARCH CENTRE. *A Methodology For Undertaking BPEO Studies of Sewage Treatment and Disposal.* WRc Report PRD 2305-M/1. December 1990.

43. GARNETT, P. AND CARLTON-SMITH, C. Operational experiences of using WISDOM in Anglian Water. Paper presented to a joint meeting of the Central Southern and Metropolitan Branches of the Institution of Water and Environmental Management, London, October 1993.

44. BROWN, M. J. AND WHIPPS, A. P. South West Water: sewage sludge utilisation and treatment strategy. In: *Proc. of European Conf. on Sludge and Organic Waste.* University of Leeds, April 1994.

45. ANDERSON, L. 'DISPEL' and its application. Paper presented to *Conf. on Sewage Sludge—from Disposal to Treatment.* London, May 1992.

INDEX

(Italic page numbers denote figures or plates)

THE LIBRARY
GUILDFORD COLLEGE
of Further and Higher Education

Author CIWEM

Title Sewage Sludge

Class 628.16 CHA

Accession 95810

95810